D1020745

VANISHING GIANTS

VANISHING GIANTS

GIANTS

The Story
of the
Sequoias

by

ROBERT SILVERBERG

SIMON AND SCHUSTER
New York

SECOND PRINTING

SBN 671-65067-X TRADE
SBN 671-65068-8 LIBRARY

LIBRARY OF CONGRESS CATALOG CARD NUMBER: 69-16876
MANUFACTURED IN THE UNITED STATES OF AMERICA
PRINTED BY MAHONY & ROESE INC., NEW YORK
BOUND BY ECONOMY BOOKBINDING CORP., NEW JERSEY

Photograph Credits

The American Museum of Natural History: pp. 15, 27, 41,
60, 63, 71, 75, 80, 83, 112, 117.

The Bettmann Archive, Inc.: pp. 89, 95, 100, 105.

State of California, Division of Beaches and Parks:
p. 131.

United States Department of the Interior, National Park Service:
jacket, frontispiece, pp. 55, 69, 135, 143.

Contents

I

The Discoverers

California, that land of wonders at the western edge of the New World, was still a place of mystery in 1769 to most white men. A few European explorers had visited its coasts and had even made short journeys inland, but none had gone very far. Certainly none of those early visitors had said anything about seeing trees taller than the greatest cathedrals of Europe.

The Spanish expedition under Juan Rodríguez Cabrillo, touring California's coast in 1542, had come to a place of thick forest, which Cabrillo named "the Cape of Pines." Cabrillo's "pines" may very well have been redwood trees; but he gave no indication that he had seen anything out of the ordinary.

Sir Francis Drake, camping near San Francisco Bay in 1579, interrupted his round-the-world voyage for some weeks, long enough to become friendly with the peaceful Indians of California and to negotiate a treaty with them. One of Drake's men wrote an account of the expedition in which he spoke of California as "a goodly country . . . stored with many blessings fit for the use of man." But though he mentioned "very large and fat deer which there we saw by thousands," and other animals, he said not a word about colossal trees. Nor did Sebastián Vizcaíno, who landed near Monterey in 1602, take any formal note of the redwood trees that must have been all about, though the narrative of his expedition describes the "tall oak" under which Mass was said.

The honor of informing the world about California's redwoods thus fell to a latecomer among explorers: Gaspar de Portolá, who was sent out from Mexico in 1768 to colonize California on behalf of Spain. Portolá brought with him several Franciscan priests to establish missions in the newly settled land; among them was Junípero Serra, the great missionary who became known as the Apostle of California.

Portolá began his journey in the peninsula of Lower California, then as now a part of Mexico. Traveling northward overland, he crossed what would one day be the boundary between Mexico and the United States, and arrived at San Diego on July 1, 1769. There Father Serra founded the mission at San Diego, the first in California, and two weeks later the expedition continued north, heading along the coast toward Monterey.

A priest named Juan Crespi kept the official diary of the Portolá expedition. In October 1769, the explorers came upon a grove of remarkable trees on the Pajaro River, near the present-day town of Watsonville on the Bay of Monterey. Father Crespi wrote that the Spaniards had traveled

> over plains and low hills, well forested with very high trees of a red color, of a species unknown to us. They have a very different leaf from cedars, and although the wood resembles cedar somewhat in color, it is very different and is without a cedar odor; moreover the wood of the trees that we have

found is very brittle. In this region there is great abundance of these trees and, as we knew not the names of the trees, we gave them that of the color of their wood, *palo colorado*, "red wood."

This was the first written description of one of the botanical wonders of the world, the splendid redwood tree of the California coast, the tallest and perhaps most noble tree on Earth. Another member of the Portolá expedition, one Miguel Costanso, noted in his diary that the redwoods were "the largest, highest, and straightest trees we had seen up to that time; some of them were four or five yards in diameter [the distance straight through the trunk from side to side]. The wood is of a dull dark reddish color, very soft, brittle, and full of knots."

It is hard to understand why Costanso and Father Crespi thought the redwood's wood was brittle. Actually, redwood timber, while soft and easy to cut and shape, is wood of the highest quality. That redwoods would be valuable sources of lumber was guessed by the next man to write of them, Father Pedro Font, who kept the journal of a later expedition to San Francisco Bay. On March 26, 1776, Father Font wrote that his party had seen "a few trees which they call redwood, a tree that is certainly beautiful; and I believe that it is very useful for its timber for it is very straight and tall. . . ."

Three days later, the explorers caught sight of a tree in the distance which, said Father Font, was "a very high redwood . . . rising like a great tower." When they reached the tree on March 30, Father Font measured it and found it to be 137 feet 6 inches high, or taller than a twelve-story building; its circumference, its distance around the base, was 14 feet 9 inches. These are modest proportions for a redwood, in fact; but Father Font was awed by his *palo alto*, his "tall tree," even though the soldiers told him "they had seen even larger ones in the mountains." More than a century later a town was founded at this site, some 28 miles southeast of San Francisco, and it was named Palo Alto for Father Font's tree, which still stands.

As the Spanish settlements spread through California, it became known that these giant trees existed in fantastic numbers along the coast. They did not seem to thrive far south of San Francisco, but from there northward they stretched in one mighty forest hundreds of miles long. It was a narrow forest, though; the redwoods seemed to require a cool, moist environment, and they grew only in a coastal strip 10 to 40 miles wide that was reached by chilly fogs drifting in from the Pacific Ocean.

Through this range the redwoods formed groves so dense that few trees of other kinds could be found in them. Dark red-brown trunks rose straight as pillars; often there were no branches for the first 100 or 150 feet of a tree's height, and only by looking far up into the forest's distant canopy could one see the heavy boughs that bore the short, stubby green needles and the tiny cones, both less than an inch long.

The Spaniards made little use of their redwood empire. They preferred to build their missions and dwellings of adobe, or dried mud, as they had learned to do from the Pueblo Indians of what is now New Mexico. However, they did cut down a few redwoods to use for the heavy beams of their largest buildings. They recognized the beauty and the durability of the wood; Father Junípero Serra, when he lay on his deathbed in 1784, asked to be buried in a redwood coffin. His request was honored, and he was laid to rest at Mission San Carlos Borromeo, in Carmel. In time the church fell into ruins, and Father Serra's coffin disappeared in the debris. But it was discovered again ninety-eight years after his burial, and the wood proved to be in perfect condition.

The redwoods were so huge that logging them appeared impossible. One could ride through a forest in which tree after tree was 200, 250, 300 feet tall. Even a small redwood was vastly bigger than the greatest trees in Spain. The settlers had never seen such monsters before. And the redwoods were so thick through the trunk that, as one of Portolá's men wrote, "eight men all holding hands could not span one of them." One Spaniard rode his horse into a hollow place in the trunk of a redwood and exclaimed, "Now I have a house in case it rains!" To cut down such enormous trees seemed an impossible challenge.

Strangely, that challenge had been accepted by the Indians of California—easygoing primitive folk, among the most backward of all the natives of North America. Living among the awesome redwoods for centuries before the white man discovered them, these Indians had made use of the wood of fallen trees, and then had begun to cut down some of the forest titans even though they had no metal tools whatever.

It was a task calling for immense patience. The Indians would press heated stones against one side of a tree to make a hole: slow work, for the stout bark and strong wood yielded only stubbornly to fire. Using scrapers made of the horns of elk, the Indians would cut away the charred wood and press their hot stones once more against the tree, until at last a gaping hole had been made. Then they would begin the process on the other side of the trunk, higher up; and when the tree had been weakened sufficiently by these nibbles, gravity would do the rest of the job, pulling it over. The Indians knew how to plan their logging so as to control the direction in which the tree would fall, and they cleared the ground, arranging a bed of logs to cushion the forest monarch's collapse and spare the timber from harm.

When a tree finally had been felled, it had to be cut into sections of a size that could be handled, and this was done in the same painstaking way, with heated stones and elkhorn scrapers. Next the Indians cut the rough logs into planks by driving wedges of wood and elkhorn into their ends. Finally the planks were smoothed with stone adzes, which are axes with their blades mounted at right angles to the shafts so that they can be used for scraping and hollowing logs. It took an entire village many months to cut down one tree, and so redwood boards were highly valued commodities among the Indians. Neither they nor the Spaniards made any real inroads into the incredible, seemingly inexhaustible forests of these astonishing trees. Well into the nineteenth century the population of California could be numbered in the thousands; trees outnumbered men by a wide margin.

The redwoods received their first serious scientific attention in 1794. Great Britain had sent out an expedition to the Pacific three years earlier under the command of Captain George Vancouver; he went by way of Australia, New Zealand, and the Pacific islands to North America, carrying out a careful survey of the coast of what is now Washington State and British Columbia. After a voyage around the large island that bears his name, Vancouver returned to the Pacific to explore Hawaii, and in April 1793 began a second tour along the North American coast. This time he sailed south past the Spanish settlements, traveling the whole length of the redwood empire. Archibald Menzies, the expedition botanist, examined the huge trees and decided that they represented a new species.

Reports of the redwood's great size excited the interest of other European botanists, who tried to find a place for the tree in their systems of classification. Since the seventeenth century, scientists had been attempting to group all living things according to their physical characteristics. The greatest achievement in this field was that of the Swedish botanist Carl Linnaeus (1707–78), whose system of classification is the basis for the one used today. Linnaeus divided all living things into two kingdoms, that of animals and that of plants; these he divided into large groups called *phyla*, from the Greek word meaning "tribe." All mammals went into one phylum, all fishes into another, all birds into a third, and so on.

The phyla were further divided into classes, the classes into orders, and the orders into *genera*, the plural of the word *genus*, meaning "race" or "sort." Animals and plants that shared certain broad, obvious characteristics made up each genus. All oak trees—black oak, white oak, red oak, and the rest—went into the genus *Quercus*. All maples were grouped in the genus *Acer*. Lions, tigers, and house cats were classed in the genus *Felis*. Dogs, foxes, and wolves were placed in the genus *Canis*.

But a house cat is quite different from a tiger, and the black oak's sharply pointed leaves can easily be told from the rounded leaves of a white oak. Linnaeus employed a further distinction, dividing each genus into a number of *species*. (The word is a Latin one, meaning "outward appearance.") To identify any particular type of living thing, Linnaeus proposed using a double name, genus plus species. The black oak was named *Quercus velutina,* and the white oak *Quercus alba*. The house cat received the scientific name of *Felis catus*, the tiger *Felis tigris*. Man was placed in the genus *Homo* and the species *sapiens*, meaning "wise."

Finding the pattern of resemblances that makes it possible to assign genus and species is not always easy. The African elephant, for example, has large ears and two finger-like projections at the end of its trunk. The Indian elephant has small ears, one projection at the end of its trunk, and a pair of bumps on its skull that the African one does not have. Zoologists still quarrel over whether to place the two types of elephant in the same genus as different species, or to put them in different genera. Classifying the redwood also proved complicated.

Plainly it belonged to the plant kingdom and to the phylum of *spermatophytes*, or flowering plants. Because of the way it produced its seeds, it could be placed in the class of *gymnosperms*, whose seeds are unprotected by a fruit or shell. Within that class, the redwood could be assigned to the order of *conifers*, which includes those trees that have evergreen needles as their leaves, and carry their seeds in cones. But the conifers are further subdivided into five families; in which of them should the redwood be listed?

In 1823 an English botanist, A. B. Lambert, showed that the redwood was related by its structure and shape of cones to an unusual tree of the Eastern United States, the bald cypress. This tree, despite its name, is not a close relative of other cypresses, and although classed with the evergreens, it sheds its needles every autumn, just as such deciduous trees as the maples and birches drop their leaves. It lives in the swamplands of the Southern states, and has a distinctive shape, with a large, knobby base and jutting "knees" that rise above the water of the swamp. Though tall in comparison to most trees, reaching a height of some 150 feet when fully grown, the bald cypress at its biggest is only about half the height of an average redwood.

Lambert put the redwood into the bald cypress's genus, *Taxodium*; and decreed that the redwood, as a newly dis-

Redwoods grow as straight as pillars. Often there are no branches for the first 100 or 150 feet.

covered species of this genus, should be known as *Taxodium sempervirens*. (*Sempervirens* means "always green" in Latin.)

Stephan Ladislaus Endlicher, a German-born botanist who lived in Vienna, disagreed with Lambert's interpretation. He too thought that the redwood was related to the bald cypress, but not so closely that the two trees could be placed in the same genus. In a large work on evergreen trees published in 1847, Endlicher created the genus *Sequoia* and named the redwood *Sequoia sempervirens,* which it still remains.

Why he picked this name is somewhat mysterious. The usual explanation is that Endlicher named the great trees in honor of a celebrated American Indian named Sequoyah, adapting the spelling of the name slightly to follow Latin style. Sequoyah never visited California or had any connection with the trees that bear his name, and we do not know why Endlicher chose to honor him in this way. Perhaps he felt that it was somehow appropriate to name these spectacular American trees after an American Indian, and chose the only Indian whose name he happened to know.

Certainly Sequoyah deserved some imposing monument, if not precisely the one he received. He was a halfbreed, born about 1770 in what was later to become the State of Tennessee; his father was a British trader named Nathaniel Guess or Gist, and his mother was a Cherokee Indian. Raised as a Cherokee, Sequoyah never learned to speak or write English, but this did not prevent him from entering the white man's world; he served with the United States Army in 1813 and 1814, and also became skilled as a silversmith and painter.

Sequoyah, a thoughtful man, sought to understand why it was that the white man was so powerful. He decided that the secret was written language, which enabled the white man to collect knowledge and transmit it to others. No Indians, not even the highly civilized ones of Mexico and Peru, had ever invented a true system of writing—and this, Sequoyah felt, was the reason why his mother's people had lost their lands to the white-skinned conquerors from Europe. About 1809 he began to invent a written language for the Cherokees, and after a dozen years of work he produced the 86-letter Cherokee alphabet; he is the only man in history known to have developed a usable alphabet by himself.

Actually Sequoyah's alphabet was not an alphabet at all, but a syllabary. That is, instead of using one symbol for each sound, as our alphabet does, it employed one symbol per syllable. A syllabary has separate characters to represent such syllables as "ra," "ro," "re," "ru," and "ri," for example, whereas we write those syllables with combinations of our basic letters. Sequoyah's system, though, was efficient and easy to learn. He taught it to his fellow tribesmen, and soon it was being used by Cherokees in many parts of the country; books and newspapers in the Cherokee language were published, and Sequoyah himself was hailed as one of the outstanding members of his race. By the time of his death in 1843 he was perhaps the most famous Indian in the country—and possibly that is why Stephan Endlicher gave his name, four years later, to the colossal trees of California.

Sequoia sempervirens went into the scientific books as the redwood's technical name, but the marvelous tree of California remained almost unknown to the general world, a distant wonder that few people had ever seen. That was about to change, though; a year after Endlicher's book was published, gold was discovered in California, and a year after that the population of that distant region began a sudden and dramatic climb.

A Swiss adventurer named John Augustus Sutter, who

had come to the United States in 1834 to seek his fortune, had settled in California five years later. California then belonged to Mexico, which had won its independence from Spain not long before, and Sutter took out Mexican citizenship in 1840. The following year the Mexican authorities granted him 76 square miles of California, which Sutter turned into a little kingdom. He built a fort, a trading post, a flour mill, and a sawmill, set up farms and ranches, and became a central figure in the still-small colony of pioneers who were moving to California from the Eastern United States.

In the fall of 1847 Sutter hired a carpenter named James Marshall to build a new sawmill for him on the American River, some 60 miles northeast of Sacramento. For several months Marshall and his workmen toiled to construct a dam to provide power for the mill; and one day in January 1848, while inspecting the river channel near the dam site, Marshall saw the glitter of gold six inches beneath the surface of the water.

Marshall carried the news to Sutter, who tried to keep it a secret, knowing that a gold rush would bring a mob of wild, greedy, destructive prospectors through his territory. But the news leaked out. Mining fever spread like an epidemic through California, which the United States had taken from Mexico that year; and when the story of the gold of Sutter's Mill reached New York at the end of the year, shiploads of gold seekers set out at once. By February of 1849 the first of these would-be treasure hunters—the "forty-niners," they were nicknamed—began to appear in San Francisco.

San Francisco was then a collection of shabby shacks and it had a population of perhaps a thousand. But as the forty-niners poured in—some coming by sea all the way around

Cape Horn, and others traveling overland via "prairie schooner"—the village became a town, and the town a city. San Francisco was the gateway to the gold-mining country. During 1849 about 50,000 prospectors came to California; by the end of 1852 California had a population of 250,000, fifteen times as many as in 1848, and San Francisco had swelled to a mighty metropolis of some 100,000 souls.

All these newcomers needed houses—and the redwoods began to topple.

At first redwood timber was regarded with scorn. It seemed too soft, too light, to men accustomed to the harder woods of the East. They ignored the magnificent groves of redwood along the coast and went to the trouble and expense of importing timber and even whole houses around Cape Horn. The redwood forests seemed mere nuisances that got in the way of the search for gold. Two forty-niners named Rogers and Wood, exploring the area east of Trinidad in northern California, found a forest of redwoods "from 5 to 15 feet in diameter, and tall in proportion to the thickness," with thick underbrush all about. They wrote:

> Through this forest we could not travel to exceed two miles a day. The reason of this was the immense quantity of fallen timber that lay upon the ground in every conceivable shape and direction and in many instances one piled upon another so that the only alternative left was literally to cut our way through. . . . For three long weary days did we toil in these redwoods. . . .
>
> At length we issued from this dismal forest prison in which we had so long been shut up, into the open country, and at the same instant in full view of that vast world of water—the Pacific Ocean.

The redwoods were the answer to the forty-niners' housing shortage, though. At Fort Ross, near Cape Mendocino, a

Russian colony established in 1812 had been built entirely of redwood: church, stockade, and all the dwellings. The Russians, who had settled there to hunt sea otters for their valuable fur, had left in 1841 after virtually wiping out the otters, and had sold their colony to John Sutter; the handsome redwood structures attracted attention, and soon were being imitated all along the California coast. Redwood no longer was scorned. Not only was it cheap and incredibly abundant but, the forty-niners were discovering, the attractive timber would not rot, was not bothered by termites, took paint well, was easy to work, and had an unusual degree of resistance to fire.

By 1850 sawmills were in operation on the hills south of San Francisco, and San Francisco itself, growing at a frantic rate, became a city of redwood houses. Soon most of the groves near the city had been logged away, and it became necessary for San Francisco to fetch timber from the forests farther north. The hastily built wooden city was prone to fires, and was devastated several times despite the redwood's ability to withstand conflagrations; each time the city burned down it was swiftly rebuilt, and the demand for redwood timber soared higher.

No one paused long to admire the beauty of the redwood groves. The madness of the gold fever gripped everyone. In 1852 alone, some $81,000,000 in gold came from California's mines, spurring thousands of new and hopeful prospectors to head west and try their luck. In the wild atmosphere of the gold rush, the redwood trees were just incidental features of the background, which happened to be handy for converting into shingles, fence posts, houses, barns, piers, water tanks, or anything else the settlers might need. They were big trees, yes, but they did not seem to be special cause for wonder in a land where everything was so much larger than normal.

Then, at the height of the gold rush, there came news from California's mountainous interior of a gigantic tree that managed to make *Sequoia sempervirens* look scrawny by comparison. This super-sequoia was so fantastic that even the gold hunters took time out from their search for the yellow metal to examine it.

II

The Giant Sequoias of the Sierra Nevada

Most of the men who sought gold passed through San Francisco, but there were no mines there. The mines were inland, along the western slopes of California's rugged Sierra Nevada mountain range. Long ago, volcanic action had flushed rivers of hot water along those slopes—water that carried in it suspended particles of dissolved gold. The water passed through the quartz of the mountains, dropping its burden of gold on its way. The precious metal formed a giant lode, or deposit, some 200 miles in length.

As centuries passed, streams rushing down the mountains cut loose fragments of gold and swept them into the brooks and creeks of the Sacramento Valley. There, in the middle of the nineteenth century, gold was literally for the taking. The prospectors simply had to scoop up the sand and gravel of the stream beds, sift it with care, and pluck out the flakes or nuggets of gold. The only investment anyone needed was a "washbowl," or flat basin, to use in panning for gold.

Out from San Francisco rushed a torrent of treasure hunters who built flimsy camps for themselves in the Sierra

Nevada foothills and spent their days hip-deep in water and their nights in revelry. The mining camps were grimy, sordid places with picturesque names—names like Fleatown, Whiskey Gulch, You Bet, Boomo Flat, and Shirttail Canyon. Fortunes were made in the streams in the afternoons and lost at the gambling tables in the evenings. When the gold of one region played out, the miners moved along to another site, leaving behind the deserted buildings of their camp to become a ghost town.

One of the liveliest mining camps of the Sierra Nevada in the spring of 1852 was Murphy's Camp in Calaveras County. John Murphy and his brother Dan had been among the first of the "forty-niners"—in fact, they had been trying their luck as early as the summer of 1848—and by 1852 they had made themselves millionaires several times over. Murphy's Camp was located in the midst of what seemed like an inexhaustible goldfield, and it had attracted a miscellaneous crew of generally disreputable gold seekers.

The primitive method of panning for gold with a hand-held washbasin had given way by then to mechanized prospecting: it was quicker and far more profitable to shovel large quantities of stream gravel into a big wooden trough called a "long tom," and send water through it at high velocity to separate the gold from the dirt. The watery cascades washed away the sand and gravel and left the glittering metal in the long tom. But it took plenty of water to run such an operation, more water than the skimpy stream at Murphy's Camp could supply. So a group of miners banded together to form the Union Water Company, which undertook to build an aqueduct to fetch water from the Stanislaus River, 15 miles away.

It was a big job. The Stanislaus was upcountry, high in the Sierra Nevada, and a system of trestles and bridges was needed to bring the aqueduct across the canyons and gorges that lay between Murphy's Camp and the river. Loggers had to be brought in to fell trees; an army of carpenters arrived to cut the trees into boards. For a while there were more construction workers than prospectors in Murphy's Camp. To feed them all, the water company hired four hunters to bring in a supply of meat. Before long, these hunters had emptied the nearby forests of game, and were forced to roam ever farther from the camp—which is how one of the hunters, A. T. Dowd, came to discover the giant sequoias on an April day in 1852.

Dowd had gone deep into the wooded country southeast of Murphy's Camp, near the Stanislaus River, and had wounded a grizzly bear that fled into the forest. Dowd was following the bear's track and concentrating so intently on his prey that at first he did not notice the changing character of the trees around him. Suddenly he found himself in front of a tree that could scarcely be ignored. At ground level its reddish trunk was as wide as a house, and it rose, scarcely tapering at all, until its crown was lost to view at an incredible distance overhead. The tree had no branches for the first hundred feet or so of its height; the branches that sprouted higher up were each of them the size of an ordinary tree.

Dowd had seen the redwoods of the coast, which grew even taller than this tree; but those redwoods, while far more massive than any trees of the East, seemed almost dainty compared with this giant. The coast redwoods had slender trunks, at least in proportion to their great height; the tree before him was unbelievably broad, a veritable wall of wood many yards across, an auburn tower that lacked grace but was almost terrifying in its mightiness. A redwood of the coast might be thought of as an enlarged version of the familiar spruces and firs of other regions, but no tree could be compared to this one in shape, proportions, or immensity.

Other trees of the same kind could be seen farther off. Dowd put his wounded bear completely out of his mind. He stared at the stupendous tree until he began to persuade himself that it was real; and then he wondered how he was going to bring the news to the men of Murphy's Camp. If he showed up and announced that he had found the largest tree in the world, the miners and construction men might simply shrug and ignore it. If he tried to describe the tree, giving some idea of its unbelievable bulk as well as its height, they would tell him he was drunk. This was an era when telling tall tales was a popular sport, and Dowd knew his story would sound like just another mining-country myth.

Still, he went back to Murphy's Camp and spoke of what he had found. The reaction was just about what he had expected: the men laughed and jeered, and the more earnestly he swore that he was speaking the truth, the more he was ridiculed. Dowd brooded for a while, trying to think of some way to persuade a few of the scoffers to come into the forest and see for themselves. But no one was going to walk 15 or 20 miles just to see a tree, especially so unlikely a tree as the one Dowd claimed he had discovered.

So he waited until the mockery had died down, and the men of the camp had stopped joking about his super-tree. Then, one Sunday morning, he rushed into the settlement in great excitement, announcing loudly that he had just shot "the largest grizzly bear that I ever saw in my life." He had left the bear dead in the forest, he said, and needed help getting it back to camp.

Some skeptics, perhaps, remembered that this was the same man who had claimed only a short time before to have found a mammoth tree. But no one commented on Dowd's strange knack for coming on gigantic things in the forest. It was, after all, his business to hunt; and grizzly-bear meat was a delicacy. There were no accusations of a hoax this time. The men could practically smell those bear steaks sizzling on the fire. With much glee, the whole camp turned out to help Dowd haul his monster bear to town.

He led them on and on, through thickly wooded glades and over deep canyons and up steep ridges. Finally they rounded a bend in the woods and came to Dowd's tree. It was an overpowering sight. There stood a tree whose trunk was wide enough to fill a broad San Francisco avenue from curb to curb, a tree whose lofty rounded crown made dwarfs out of the pines and firs—themselves magnificent by ordinary standards—that were its forest neighbors.

"Now do you believe my big-tree story?" Dowd yelled. "This is the big grizzly bear I wanted you to see. Do you still think it's a yarn?"

The miners forgave Dowd for his trick. They crowded around the tree, measuring themselves against it in disbelief, fingering its knobby base, squinting up at the distant branches. James M. Hutchings, who was there, wrote in his 1860 book, *Scenes of Wonder and Curiosity in California*, that the rough miners "stood speechless with profound awe . . . under these forest giants."

Dowd had discovered what now is called the Calaveras Grove, today a part of Calaveras Big Trees State Park, California. More than 150 of the huge trees were clustered in a 50-acre area, and more than half of them were 10 feet or more in diameter. News of the amazing trees swiftly reached the outside world. As Hutchings put it, "But a short time

The General Grant Tree, which has a base circumference of 107.6 feet and a base diameter of 40.3 feet, is the thickest of all living giant sequoias.

was allowed to elapse after the discovery of this remarkable grove, before the trumpet-tongued press proclaimed the wonder to all sections of the State, and to all parts of the world, and the lovers of the marvelous began first to doubt, then to believe, and afterwards to flock to see with their own eyes the objects of which they had heard so much."

One thing that emerged in the early excitement over the big trees of the Sierra Nevada was that Dowd had not really been their discoverer. Sightseers who came to the grove later in 1852 found a tree in whose bark had been carved the inscription *J. M. Wooster, June 1850*. Newspapermen investigated the story and learned that a certain J. Marshall Wooster had lived at Murphy's Camp that year. Wooster himself soon turned up to say that he had visited the grove of giants in the company of one William Quirk and a man named Sanburn, but that he could not claim credit for its discovery. Two other men from Murphy's Camp, he said, had set out on May 20, 1850, and had found the grove while hunting; he and his two companions had gone to see it twelve days later upon hearing of it. One of the discoverers, Wooster said, was named Whitehead, and he could not recall the name of the other.

Whitehead and his forgotten friend may have been the first white men to see the Calaveras Grove, but, as it turned out years later, not even they were the first white men to behold the big trees. That honor belongs to the members of an expedition from Great Salt Lake, Utah, to California in 1833, led by F. R. Walker—the first white men to cross the Sierra Nevada from east to west. A Pennsylvanian named Zenas Leonard, one of Walker's men, kept a journal of the expedition which was published in 1839 at Clearfield, Pennsylvania. In Leonard's book the following statement appeared:

In the last two days travelling we have found some trees of the red-wood species, incredibly large—some of which would measure from 16 to 18 fathoms round the trunk at the height of a man's head from the ground.

One tree alone has such dimensions—for 16 fathoms is 96 feet—and Zenas Leonard could have been referring only to the giant sequoia. At the time the Walker expedition found the big trees, it was passing through what is now Yosemite National Park, some 50 miles southeast of Dowd's Calaveras Grove. However, Leonard's book, which was only 87 pages long and appeared in an extremely small edition, went almost unnoticed when it was published, and was forgotten altogether for many years. Not until 1904, when it was rediscovered and reissued by a Cleveland publisher, did Zenas Leonard win recognition as the first man to have described the Sierra Nevada giants in print.

III
The Naming of Names

Two forest giants now were known to exist in California; and scientists on two continents swiftly became embroiled in controversy over the classification and technical name of the Sierra titan. What was the big tree's relationship to that other giant, the coast redwood, *Sequoia sempervirens*, which had been known for nearly a century? Where did the Sierra tree fit into the general order of evergreen trees?

The first attempt at scientific classification of the Sierra Nevada giant was made by Albert Kellogg and Herman Behr, of the California Academy of Natural Sciences. They recognized that the new big trees, like the redwoods of the coast, were more closely related to the bald cypress than to any other tree. Therefore they put the big tree into the genus *Taxodium* and called it *Taxodium giganteum*. In this they were following the system of A. B. Lambert of Great Britain, who, thirty years before, had named the redwood *Taxodium sempervirens*. (They were not aware, evidently, that Stephan Endlicher's book of 1847 had taken the redwood out of the genus *Taxodium* and put it into a genus of its own as *Sequoia sempervirens*.)

European botanists learned of the big trees for the first time in July 1853, when reports from the Calaveras Grove reached England. The tree was described as having overlapping scalelike leaves similar to those of junipers and cedars; and for a while the British referred to it as a giant cedar. Late in 1853, though, the plant collector William Lobb sent seeds, branches, and a living seedling of the big tree to England, and within months it was clear that the differences between the California tree and the known cedars were greater than the resemblances. (Lobb's seeds were planted in many parts of England and Scotland, and the cool, rainy climate proved quite suitable for the tree. Today there are numerous giant sequoias growing in Great Britain, some of them over 100 feet in height and 4 feet thick at the base.)

Some of Lobb's specimens came into the hands of John Lindley, professor of botany at University College, London, who was considered to be Britain's foremost authority on the plant kingdom. Lindley showed that it was incorrect to class the big tree with the cedars, and that it should not even be placed in the same genus as its relative, the bald cypress. Nor did he choose to put it in the genus *Sequoia* along with the coast redwood. Lindley proposed creating a special genus for the great tree; and he selected a name that would honor the outstanding British military hero of the era, the Duke of Wellington. Wellington, who had died in September 1852, had won his first fame serving in India at the beginning of the nineteenth century, and then had become the British commander in the long war against Napoleon's France. His moment of greatest glory had come at the battle of Waterloo, in 1815, at which he ended Napoleon's power; afterward he had held a variety of important governmental posts, including that of Prime Minister.

In announcing the proposed name for the giant tree, Lindley declared:

> We think that no one will differ from us in feeling that the most appropriate name to be proposed for the most gigantic tree which has been revealed to us by modern discovery is that of the greatest of modern heroes. Wellington stands as high above his contemporaries as the California tree above all the surrounding foresters. Let it then bear henceforward the name of WELLINGTONIA GIGANTEA.

Quite naturally Lindley's suggested name for the tree aroused resentment in the United States, where few people thought that "the most appropriate name to be proposed" should be that of a British military hero. In 1854, Dr. C. F. Winslow published an article in the *California Farmer* attacking Lindley's proposal. Let us at least name the forest colossus for a great American instead of a great Briton, he said; and he dubbed the tree *Washingtonia gigantea.*

The purpose of giving scientific names to living things is to simplify discussion of them; in theory, the first scientific name coined for a newly discovered species is universally accepted so that scientists everywhere will know which particular species is meant when the name appears in a technical work. But in this case, less than two years after the first reports of the gigantic trees were published, three different Latin names had been applied to them!

The situation rapidly grew more complicated. Sir William Jackson Hooker, director of the Royal Botanical Garden at Kew, said that Lindley had erred in putting the Sierra Nevada giant in a genus by itself. The big tree belonged in the same genus as the coast redwood, he said. Since Stephan Endlicher had given that genus the name *Sequoia,* Hooker said that the new giant should be a species of *Sequoia* too.

French botanists agreed. The French consul in San Francisco had sent specimens of the big tree to Paris in 1854. In June of that year the botanist Joseph Decaisne exhibited them at a meeting of the Botanical Society of France and pointed out the similarities between the giant and the coast redwood. The botanists of France cast their votes in favor of a single genus for both trees, and approved the name suggested by Decaisne, *Sequoia gigantea*, for the Sierra Nevada tree. (It is probably unfair to say so, but the French may have taken a certain pleasure in refusing to endorse the British suggestion, *Wellingtonia gigantea,* since the Duke of Wellington had been the archenemy of France.)

Patriots on both sides of the Atlantic stuck to their positions. Most British botanists clung to *Wellingtonia gigantea*; all American botanists insisted on *Washingtonia gigantea*; the French and other European botanists preferred the neutral *Sequoia gigantea*. After a while, all but the diehards gave up a little ground. Americans began using the name *Sequoia washingtonia* and the British coined *Sequoia wellingtonia*. Well into the twentieth century all three names were used for the Sierra Nevada tree, but gradually *Sequoia gigantea* was adopted by a majority of botanists everywhere.

In 1939, when the problem seemed resolved, J. T. Bucholz conducted a detailed study of the two members of the genus *Sequoia* and decided that they were not so closely related after all. He proposed that the Sierra Nevada giant be taken out of *Sequoia* and put into an entirely new genus under the name *Sequoiadendron giganteum*. The scientific reaction to this suggestion was not particularly enthusiastic. Today a few technical books do use this name, but *Sequoia gigantea* is more commonly employed. *Sequoia sempervirens* remains, as it has been since Endlicher in 1847, the only technical name used for the redwoods of the Pacific Coast.

VANISHING GIANTS

Efforts to agree on a popular name for the two members of the genus *Sequoia* have been equally confused and muddled. Anyone who has seen both trees knows that they really do not look much like each other, yet millions of Americans know vaguely that there are two kinds of giant tree in California, without having any notion which is which.

The trouble is that the trees have been given too many different popular names, and those names have been used much too loosely.

Most Californians refer to the Sierra Nevada *Sequoia gigantea* as the "big tree," and *Sequoia sempervirens* of the Coast as the "redwood." Many botanists refer to the trees as the "Sierra redwood" and the "coast redwood." The United States Government, which in not too many years will probably be the owner and custodian of all the remaining giant trees of both species, recommends calling them the "giant sequoia" and the "redwood," and perhaps those are the designations that deserve to be universally adopted, lest someday we are stuck with a tongue twister like "Sierra sequoia" by way of compromise. At any rate, in the chapters ahead, the term "sequoia," by itself, can refer to either tree. "Giant sequoia" is used to mean the bulky *Sequoia gigantea* of the Sierra Nevada slopes, and "redwood" refers to the graceful *Sequoia sempervirens* of the Pacific Coast.

IV
Sempervirens and Gigantea: Their Pedigree

The giant sequoia and the redwood are the world's largest trees, and are among the most long-lived. They belong to a genus whose pedigree is longer than that of nearly all other trees, going back to a time when the oaks and maples and other leafy trees of today had not yet evolved, when modern pines and cedars and hemlocks were still unknown, when man himself was far in the future. More than 100 million years ago, trees of the genus *Sequoia* that were not very different from today's redwoods and big trees grew in thick stands all over the Northern Hemisphere, in an era when dinosaurs thundered across the earth.

The earliest plant forms of all were simple one-celled ones, bacteria and algae, that developed in the sea a billion years ago or more. Much later—perhaps 350 million years ago—plants and animals began to leave the sea for the land. The flat, scaly plants known as lichens were the first to arrive on shore, anchoring themselves to rocks. More complex kinds of plants evolved in the millions of years that followed. Some were leafless and sent up short fleshy stems;

others had woody stems a foot or two in height, and sprouted flat, scalelike, overlapping leaves. These primitive plants reproduced by forming tiny one-celled bodies called spores, which were able to separate from the parent plant and develop into new organisms.

Spores should not be confused with seeds, although both play a role in the reproduction of plants. Seeds are produced only by highly developed plants which evolved relatively recently in the world's history. These plants have sexes just as animals do, and seeds are produced when a male cell fertilizes a female cell. Plants which produce spores are all of one sex, and no fertilization is needed.

Such spore producers as the ferns, horsetails, and club mosses dominated the swampy forests of 250 million years ago, long before any seed-bearing plants had evolved. The coal we use today was formed from the fossil remains of these ancient forests. During this warm, humid time, a new group of ferns appeared. Instead of spores, they carried true seeds. Some of these seed ferns grew 30 feet high, with trunks 3 feet thick. There were about 50 different species of them; the last seed ferns became extinct in the Upper Jurassic period, about 130 million years ago.

By then, other more highly developed seed producers had evolved. These were the *spermatophytes*, which botanists regard as the most highly evolved phylum in the plant kingdom, corresponding to the mammals of the animal world. Mammals house their young within the mother's body, sheltering the immature offspring until they are ready to go forth into the world. This distinguishes them from fishes or amphibians, which scatter hundreds or thousands of unprotected eggs, only a few of which may survive. Although the comparison cannot be pushed too far, the spermatophytes also take special precautions to protect their young. Each

newly forming plant is sheltered within a seed and sur-
rounded with nutritious material. Often a protective covering encloses the seed—the embryo oak in its acorn, the little
peanut in its shell, the young pea in its pod. Some spermatophytes wrap their seeds in fleshy fruits in addition to the
protective covering, so that their seeds will be seized and
carried to places where they have the best chances of sprouting: apples, berries, grapes, and tomatoes are familiar examples of this.

Spermatophytes whose seeds have an outer covering are
called *angiosperms*, "covered-seeded plants," from the
Greek words meaning "vessel" and "seed." But the angiosperms—a large class that includes the oak, the peanut, the
pea, and all other flowering plants and shrubs and leafy
trees—were the most recent of all plants to evolve. The
sequoias belong to a more primitive and much more ancient
group of spermatophytes: the *gymnosperms*, or "naked-
seeded plants."

Gymnosperms are so named because they give little or no
protection to their seeds. The little seeds may be enclosed
in a cone while developing, but when the cone opens they
have no other covering. The extinct seed ferns were gymnosperms; other members of the group today include such
uncommon plants as the palmlike cycads, the strange *Wel-
witschia* of the South African desert, the gingko tree, and
the *Gnetum* plants, which are woody shrubs that live in the
tropics and in some arid lands. But the best-known and by
far the largest order of the gymnosperms is the one that includes the evergreen trees—the pines, the hemlocks, the
firs, for example, and the sequoias.

Botanists prefer to call these evergreens *conifers*, or
"cone-bearing" trees, since the term evergreen is misleading.
The larch and bald cypress are "evergreen" gymnosperms

that drop their leaves in winter; the live oak and rhododendron are angiosperms that keep their leaves all year. And yet there are problems of consistency even in using the term conifer, since not all conifers are cone-bearing; yews and junipers, for example, enclose their seeds in berries! They are conifers nevertheless, because they share all other important characteristics of this group.

Conifers are sturdy trees. They are found on mountain slopes and highlands where no angiosperm trees can grow; they withstand savage extremes of temperature; and under the right conditions many conifers, not just the sequoias, grow to immense size. The rain-swept forests of the American Northwest are thick with such conifers as ponderosa pine, Douglas fir, and Lawson cypress which reach well over 200 feet in height, dwarfing the biggest Eastern trees; these titans fail to get their due attention only because the sequoias are even bigger. The seven most abundant trees in the forests of the United States—Douglas fir, yellow pine, redwood, cedar, hemlock, white pine, and spruce—are all conifers.

There are some five hundred species of conifers altogether. Most of them have small scalelike or needlelike leaves, though some pines have extremely long needles; and most of them remain green all year round and bear their seeds in cones. Botanists have arranged the conifers into five families, not without plenty of disagreement about which tree goes where.

The largest of the conifer families is the pine, typified by sharp needlelike leaves and woody cones. This family includes not only the many kinds of pine, but also the spruces, hemlocks, firs, larches, the true cedars or cedars of Lebanon, and some others. Most of the other trees that we call cedars are placed in the second largest conifer family, that of the cypresses. This group, marked generally by extremely short needles or flat overlapping scales, includes such trees as the junipers, the cypresses, the red and white cedars, and the arbor vitae.

Many of the short evergreens with thick, glossy needles frequently seen as garden shrubs belong to the third family, the yew. Their bright scarlet berries make them unusual among the conifers. Even more unusual are the members of the fourth conifer family, the araucarias. There are a dozen trees in this family, native to Australia, New Guinea, and Chile; some of them have been transplanted to California, Florida, and other parts of the United States where the climate is not too harsh for them. An Australian tree, the bunya-bunya, is sometimes seen in the United States; it has stiff flattened needles several inches long arranged in double rows. Its cousin, the monkey puzzle tree, is an unforgettable sight; its branches, which twist and bend at odd angles, are completely covered with stiff wedge-shaped overlapping leaves an inch or two long, which give it a formidably bristly and unclimbable look. The Norfolk Island pine, another araucaria with an attractive and distinctive shape, is sometimes cultivated as an indoor plant in colder climates.

Since the first member of the fifth conifer family to be described scientifically was *Taxodium distichum*, the bald cypress, the entire family is known to botanists as the *Taxodiaceae*. To the layman, however, it is the redwood family.

Just as the pine family includes more than pines, the redwood family includes more than redwoods—but not much more. Only three members, the bald cypress, the redwood, and the giant sequoia, are native to the United States. From Japan comes *Cryptomeria japonica*, an important and abundant timber tree that is now cultivated in the Southern United States, where it is sometimes called Japanese cedar.

Though a large tree by ordinary standards, it never reaches the giant dimensions of the sequoias. A Chinese relative is *Glyptostrobus pensilis*, the Chinese water pine—a small tree of southeastern China, more nearly akin to the bald cypress than to the sequoias.

These are virtually the only remaining trees of a family that was far-ranging and important fifty million years ago; all of them are now limited to relatively small regions of the world.

The fossil record shows that ancestors of these trees existed as early as the Upper Jurassic period, 130 million years ago, and were among the first spermatophytes to appear. Our great mountain ranges—the Rockies, the Andes, the Himalayas, the Alps—were then unformed. The continents had not assumed their modern shapes, so that a map of the Jurassic world would seem to us to be a map of some other planet. Western North America, from California to Alaska, was covered by water.

Through the strange Jurassic landscape marched ponderous dinosaurs, bizarre and massive, like living tanks: *Stegosaurus*, with great bony plates sprouting from his back, and *Brontosaurus*, fifty tons of sluggish flesh, and *Allosaurus*, with daggerlike teeth and fierce clutching claws. In the sea swam *Plesiosaurus*, fifty feet long and mostly neck, and the giant fishlike *Ichthyosaurus*. Huge flying reptiles soared on batlike wings, and toothy *Archaeopteryx,* the first true bird, fluttered through the forest branches.

The forests of 130 million years ago were unlike any we know today. Neither birch nor maple nor oak could be found anywhere in the world; cycads and giant ferns and gingko

Ancestors of these trees existed long before oaks and elms and maples. One million years ago they covered the Northern Hemisphere.

trees were there instead, and among them were some conifers, ancestors of today's pines and cedars. And—so the
fossil record tells us—ancestors of the sequoia were there
too. They spread across most of the existing land area of the
Northern Hemisphere—across North America from the
Pacific Ocean to the Atlantic, across Europe, and on
through Asia to China and Japan.

About a dozen species of these ancient sequoias have been
identified by their fossil remains: traces of cones or leaves
or branches embedded in rock. One, *Sequoia reichenbachi*,
had cones quite similar to those of today's giant sequoia.
Another, *Sequoia langsdorfii*, was almost identical in many
ways to living redwoods.

These trees outlasted the dinosaurs, the last of which died
out sixty or seventy million years ago. Small warm-blooded
creatures, nursing their young with milk, now roved the
forests. These were the first mammals, tiny ancestors of the
horse, the dog, the camel. The gymnosperms no longer dominated the forests; leafy, flowering angiosperm trees—hickory
and ash, maple and birch—appeared. Western North America emerged from the sea; but the zone from California to
Washington was warm and wet, almost tropical, fifty million
years ago, and sequoias did not live there yet. Their future
home was then a land of fig, palm, avocado, mahogany, and
other trees now generally found only in subtropical and
tropical countries.

The sequoias, preferring cooler terrain, nevertheless occupied much of the United States. Sequoia fossils have been
found in Colorado, Wyoming, Texas, and as far east as
Pennsylvania. In Yellowstone National Park, Wyoming,
there is a petrified forest where ancient trees have been preserved, turned to stone by mineral-laden waters or covered
by the ashes of once-active volcanoes, and there are se-

quoias, fifty million years old, in that eerie forest. Fossil evidence from the same period shows sequoias in England and France, and even in Greenland, northern Siberia, the island of Spitsbergen, and on the arctic islands north of Canada. No trees of any kind now grow in those icy wastes.

The sequoias reached their peak about twenty-five million years ago, in the Miocene period, when they were the dominant forest trees across thousands of miles of the world's surface. But then the earth's climate began to grow colder and drier. Subtropical regions became temperate regions; what had been temperate zones slowly turned arctic. A general southward migration of plant and animal life began throughout the Northern Hemisphere. The sequoias disappeared from the far north, no longer habitable, and edged into such formerly tropical places as California. The oldest fossil sequoia from the foothills of the Sierra Nevada dates back about twenty million years.

The world continued to change, and still the sequoias retreated. New mountain ranges were rising; glaciers spread out to the north; some species of sequoia adapted to the changing conditions and migrated to more favorable lands, others simply died out. The sequoias of Europe were among those that became extinct. The shifting climate pushed them southward toward the Mediterranean. Finally they reached the brink of the sea and could go no farther, and they perished.

About a million and a half years ago, the gradual trend toward a colder climate ceased to be gradual; much of the world was subjected to a sudden and violent chill, and in the course of a few thousand years—only a moment in geological time—huge areas were engulfed by ice. After some hundreds of thousands of years the climate warmed again, only to turn cold once more, and then warm again; there have been at least four major ice ages in the past million and a half years, the last one ending only about ten thousand years ago. Each of them vastly speeded up the process of migration and extinction that began in the Miocene period, and caused great changes in the world's distribution of plants and animals.

The sequoias were among the chief victims of the recurring ice ages. Their empire shrank and their numbers dwindled, until only two of the dozen or more species survived, cut off from the rest of North America by the Sierra Nevada, and established themselves in the areas where they are found today. *Gigantea*, which was adapted to cold weather and heavy snow, clung to a few isolated pockets along the foothills of the Sierra. *Sempervirens*, needing cool, wet weather but unable to tolerate real cold, took up its last stand in the 500-mile-long fog belt on the Pacific Coast from northern California to southern Oregon. Both trees held on there, confined to their own territories, neither one gaining ground nor losing it, at least until man with his lust for timber stumbled into their final domains.

Sempervirens and *gigantea* are living fossils of a sort, then—survivors of a vanished prehistoric era, remnants of an earlier world, two lonely relics of what had once been a world-girdling family of trees. Of the many kinds of sequoia that had loomed high above the forests of the Jurassic and Cretaceous and Eocene and Miocene and other bygone periods, these two alone had managed to endure.

Or so it seemed until 1944, when a supposedly extinct member of the family unexpectedly came back to life.

Three years earlier, a Japanese scientist named Shigeru Miki, professor of botany at Osaka City University, had published a study of certain fossils thought to be sequoia. Earlier botanists had assigned these fossils to the genus

Sequoia because they were considered virtually identical to California's coast redwoods. Named *Sequoia disticha* and *Sequoia japonica*, they had been found in rocks up to sixty million years old.

Dr. Miki discovered some fragments of these fossils, and examined them closely. He saw that the needles and shoots were arranged in groups of two, opposite one another along the twigs, while in the living *Sequoia sempervirens*, the needles and shoots are arranged in alternating groups along the twigs to give a spiral effect. It was a small difference, but a significant one to Dr. Miki, and he proposed that the two fossil species be taken out of the genus *Sequoia* and placed in the new genus *Metasequoia*, to indicate that they were almost but not quite true sequoias. The two fossils were accordingly rechristened *Metasequoia disticha* and *Metasequoia japonica*, an event of no importance whatever except to those few scientists who specialized in the botany of extinct members of the redwood family.

In 1944, though, a Chinese forester named Wang, making a regular tour of duty on behalf of the Ministry of Agriculture of the Chinese Government, came upon a huge and unfamiliar tree near the village of Mo-tao-chi, in the province of Szechuan in west-central China. Forester Wang collected some needles and cones of the strange tree and took them to Dr. W. C. Cheng, professor of forestry at National Central University, Nanking. Dr. Cheng, realizing that the tree was one that Chinese botanists had never seen before, called in other experts, who saw something about the samples that they recognized, but were unable to determine what it was. Suddenly the truth broke through: the tree from Mo-tao-chi looked just like Dr. Miki's fossil *Metasequoia*!

The fossil had come to life. A tree that had been thought

to be extinct for at least five million years, that was known only by fossil fragments from Japan, North America, and Manchuria, still grew in a remote part of China. Though unknown to science, it was nothing remarkable to the peasants of Szechuan, who called it *shui-sha*, "water spruce." Hundreds of the trees were growing in Szechuan, the biggest of them about 105 feet high and 7 feet in diameter. The world's newspapers found room amid the war news of the day for front-page stories about the dramatic discovery of this forgotten cousin of the sequoias. The tree promptly received the nickname "dawn redwood," which added to the romantic flavor of its finding.

The dawn redwood was not identical to Dr. Miki's fossils, but it was close enough to be assigned to the same genus, as *Metasequoia glyptostroboides*. (The name means "something like a sequoia, something like a Chinese water pine.") At the time of its discovery it existed only in a 300-square-mile region of western China at altitudes of 2,100 to 4,000 feet. The climate there is generally mild, and rainfall is fairly heavy, averaging 50 inches a year. However, nearly all of that rain falls during the summer, and *Metasequoia* had adapted to the long, dry Szechuan winter by becoming deciduous, like its relative the bald cypress.

Only a geographical accident had allowed the dawn redwood to survive in China after it had disappeared from the rest of the earth. Conditions of temperature, rainfall, and geography were exceptionally favorable for it there; and the region where it grew was one of the few parts of China where population was small and farmers had not yet cleared the forests to plant crops. However, botanists took no chances with the remaining *Metasequoias*. In 1947, Boston's Arnold Arboretum provided funds for a scientific expedition to the home of the dawn redwood; seeds were gathered and planted in many parts of the United States and Europe. The tree turned out to be hardy, even in the somewhat colder climates to which it was now exposed, and to grow rapidly. Thousands of them are found now in the United States; plant nurseries advertise them as landscape decorations for homeowners. From living fossil to household tree in twenty years—that has been the surprising destiny of the dawn redwood, which has come to take its place with the mighty *Sequoia gigantea* and *sempervirens* as one of the few survivors of a noble and ancient family.

V
Sempervirens and Gigantea: Vital Statistics

A visit to a grove of either species of sequoia is an awe-inspiring experience, but the quality of what is awesome differs. In a redwood forest—say, in lovely Muir Woods, just outside San Francisco—the trees are huge, but what strikes the visitor is not their size so much as their beauty. The deep-toned chocolate trunks rise clean and straight for 300 feet or more, and often the trees grow close together, producing the effect that reminds so many viewers of the pillars of a colossal cathedral. So perfectly proportioned are the trees that one actually thinks of them as slender, though they are far more massive than the humble trees most people are familiar with.

The giant sequoia is rarely called a beautiful tree; it is too wide for its height, too bulky, altogether too huge. One does not perceive it as a member of a group; one approaches each individual tree by itself, and struggles to comprehend its immensity. The great bulging base of the tree tends to hide the fact that the trunk is arrow-straight and untapered for most of its length. The redwood can inspire wonder and reverence; the giant sequoia can be almost terrifying.

Redwood forests look very different from forests of giant sequoias. This is the naturalist François Leydet's description of a redwood grove:

> The light in the depths of the forest is dim and muted as it filters down from the canopy two or three hundred feet above. High overhead the lace-work of needles constantly changes patterns as it is ruffled by the wind—now closing up, then parting to reveal a patch of blue; here fragmenting the sun's rays into a thousand pearls of light, there letting through a slanting shaft like that from a church's stained glass window. Where touched by the sun, the redwood's dark needles glow with a golden sheen. Even in the thickest fog, the aura of the forest is mysterious rather than forbidding; then the great trunks loom out of the mists with an unreal air, ghosts from a forgotten past. . . . The ruddy pillars soar straight up, mighty beyond description, a mightiness that defies capture in printed page or photographic plate.

And this is John Muir on the giant sequoia:

> Resolute, consummate, determined in form, always beheld with wondering admiration, the Big Tree always seems unfamiliar, standing alone, unrelated, with peculiar physiognomy, awfully solemn and earnest. . . . One soon becomes acquainted with new species of pine and fir and spruce as with friendly people, shaking their outstretched branches like shaking hands, and fondling their beautiful little ones; while the venerable aboriginal Sequoia, ancient of other days, keeps you at a distance, taking no notice of you, speaking only to the winds, thinking only of the sky, looking as strange in aspect and behavior among the neighboring trees as would the mastodon or hairy elephant among the homely bears and deer. . . . There is something wonderfully attractive in this king tree, even when beheld from afar, that

draws us to it with indescribable enthusiasm; its superior height and massive smoothly rounded outlines proclaiming its character in any company; and when one of the oldest of them attains full stature on some commanding ridge, it seems the very god of the woods.

Of all the many unusual features of the sequoias, their size and their age attract the most attention. The redwood is the tallest of all trees; the giant sequoia is the bulkiest of all living things. And—with one rather odd exception—nothing lives longer than the giant of the Sierra Nevada.

In height the supremacy of *Sequoia sempervirens* goes unchallenged, despite occasional claims that taller trees have been found in other parts of the world. For example, in 1932 a South African naturalist, Eugene N. Marais, named the monkey-thorn tree, *Acacia galpinii*, as the world's tallest tree. Marais found a grove of these trees along the banks of the Magalakwin River in the district of Transvaal; most of them had died long before or had been blown over and burned, and those that lived were buried in sand to a considerable depth. According to a recent account by H. A. Lueckhoff of the Forest Research Institute, Pretoria, South Africa, "The largest standing tree at that time was carefully measured by a land surveyor. It had a height of 210 feet and a girth, 3 feet above the ground, of 78 feet, with a crown spread of approximately 180 feet. On the basis of his observation on the depth of sand . . . etc., Marais concluded that were it possible to excavate the sand away from this tree, it would have had a basal girth of approximately 146 feet and a height in the neighborhood of 400 feet! At that time the remains of considerably larger trees, which had been destroyed by hurricane or fire, were still visible."

If we could accept Marais's claim unquestioningly, the monkey-thorn trees of the Magalakwin River would have to be considered by far the largest in the world, for they would be taller than the tallest redwood and greater in circumference than the biggest giant sequoia. "Unfortunately," Lueckhoff's report continues, "these old trees have all been destroyed by fire and storm and have completely disappeared. This was confirmed by an officer of this Department who visited the area about twenty years ago." Since existing monkey-thorn trees in the Transvaal reach heights of only about 80 feet and have maximum circumferences of no more than 12 feet at the base, we have to look with some suspicion on the tale of these vanished titans.

Another tree often said to be taller than the redwood is the eucalyptus of Australia. There are many species of eucalyptus, some of which have become quite well established in California; they are slender, rapidly growing trees with narrow, tapering leaves and attractive flowers, and on their native continent they do attain great sizes. A forestry handbook published by the Australian Government declares, "Under typical conditions heights range from 175 to 250 feet, but measurements of over 350 feet have been recorded. Whilst very large diameters do occur, typical measurements are 6 to 9 feet."

Australians like to boast of 400-foot eucalyptus trees, but no actual examples have so far been produced. In 1888 rewards totaling $600 were offered to anyone who could point out a 400-foot eucalyptus; the tallest tree that was located, though, measured only 326 feet 1 inch. Many other eucalyptus giants ranging from 300 to 325 feet have since been found, but scores of redwoods exceed that figure by 20 feet or more. Botanists are still waiting for the first authenticated report of a eucalyptus that comes close to equaling the height of the tallest redwoods.

One American tree that approaches redwood level is the

Douglas fir of the Pacific Northwest. Heights of 300 feet are not at all unusual for this imposing tree, and one, at Ryderwood, Washington, stands 324 feet high, or as tall as a thirty-story building. That is the current record holder for the Douglas fir, although Canadian loggers have a tradition that in 1895 one was felled that was 417 feet tall and 25 feet in diameter at the base. This would be the tallest tree ever known. How much truth there is to the tale, though, is impossible to say; the tree may well have "grown" by 100 feet or so over the years, the way big fish do after they have been caught. Some timbermen have argued that the tree was not a Douglas fir at all, but a redwood growing north of its customary range—which, if true, would still make the redwood the pinnacle of the plant kingdom.

When we turn directly to the redwoods, though, we leave the realm of rumors and tall stories. Redwood measuring is a long-established California sport, and a good deal of effort has been expended on finding and accurately measuring a tree taller than the tallest one known at the moment.

For a long time a tree in Humboldt Redwoods State Park, California, 240 miles north of San Francisco, held the record. This is Founders Tree, dedicated to John C. Merriam, Henry Fairfield Osborn, and Madison Grant, founders of the Save-the-Redwoods League, which has done so much to spare these trees from the loggers. Founders Tree bears a plaque declaring that its circumference at chest level is 40 feet, its diameter at the same point is 12.7 feet, and its height is 346.1 feet. Actually, a remeasurement in 1963 showed that Founders Tree had grown to 352.6 feet, but by then it had lost its supremacy in the redwood world to another.

A new champion was discovered in the Rockefeller Forest of Humboldt Redwoods State Park in February 1957, and was named the Rockefeller Tree. (The Rockefeller family has long been active in purchasing redwood forests for preservation as parkland.) At chest height the Rockefeller Tree's trunk was 42 feet in circumference and 13.4 feet in diameter, and its height was 359.3 feet. Since then, storm damage has clipped this giant to a mere 356.5 feet. This is the height of a 35-story skyscraper.

The search for a record-breaker did not end there, for California holds thousands of redwoods that have never even been seen by man, let alone measured. Determining the heights of trees in a redwood forest is a tricky matter; a man standing pygmylike before a group of trees around 300 feet tall, without a clear view of their crowns, has no reliable way of judging sizes by eye, since a 350-foot tree and a 320-foot tree look equally immense from below. Even with surveying instruments, an observer can be deceived by dips or rises in the ground level.

In 1963 the National Park Service began a study of the entire redwood region, with the aid of a grant from the National Geographic Society. The aim of this work was not particularly to find record-breaking trees, but to increase our overall knowledge of the redwoods and their environment, so that they can best be protected against the inroads civilization is making on them. Nevertheless, the work produced a whole set of new altitude records.

The home of the tallest trees proved to be a grove in Redwood Creek Valley near Arcata, California. Though not far south of Prairie Creek Redwoods State Park, the Redwood Creek grove was and at this writing still is private property, belonging to the Arcata Redwood Company, a timber firm. This company, one of the most active loggers of redwoods in California, had not yet begun to harvest the titans of Redwood Creek at the time of the Park Service survey. The region was so difficult to reach that few men had even entered it. But lumber company scouts had visited it and they reported that they had seen some unusually tall trees along the eastern slope of the valley.

Dr. Paul A. Zahl, a National Geographic Society naturalist, toured this virgin stand of redwoods in October 1963, entering by way of a road newly constructed by the logging company. Looking west across Redwood Creek, he saw a cluster of great trees, dozens of which had trunks 10 feet or more in diameter, rising to awesome heights. Using an Abney level—a sighting instrument that gives approximate heights—he began to measure these mighty redwoods. "On the 12th of October," he wrote, "anyone hovering in a helicopter over Redwood Creek Valley about seven miles southeast of Orick would have seen a lone man there on the gravel bars, pounding in stakes, attaching twine, sighting through an instrument, wading the stream, disappearing into the woods, reappearing, writing in a notebook—then repeating the whole routine at other points along the stream. I had already spotted at least half a dozen trees that should be among the tallest in California's Redwood Empire."

The Abney level showed him, however, that he had been too generous. Most of the trees in the grove were about 320 feet high; some were close to 335 feet, and one approached 350 feet—splendid trees all, but no competition for the 359-foot Rockefeller Tree.

To get photographs of the lofty grove, Zahl crossed Redwood Creek and climbed a partially logged ridge on the west side of the valley; and while pausing to catch his breath, about 300 feet above the valley floor, Zahl noticed an extraordinary tree, standing somewhat inland from the stream,

Redwood Creek is the home of the tallest redwoods. A 385-foot tree, the tallest known living thing on earth, was discovered here in 1966.

that had escaped his attention before. From the valley below it had looked no taller than its neighbors; but now this redwood "rose above the others like a giant candle." He sketched its position and ran back across the creek to measure it.

Several readings from different angles gave him a rough calculation of 370 feet for the tree—so far above the record of 359 feet that he wondered if he had made some error. He went to Arcata and made arrangements for professional surveyors to visit the grove. Shortly a fourteen-man team was roaming Redwood Creek Valley, sighting treetops, computing angles, measuring base. lines, looking through books of tables. Zahl's tree was measured at 367.8 feet—making it the tallest known living thing on earth. Chester C. Brown, head of the National Park Service redwood project, found trees measuring 367.4 and 364.3 feet, giving them second and third place. The Rockefeller Tree and Founders Tree, deposed titleholders, now held fourth and fifth place; sixth place went to yet another Redwood Creek Valley tree, measuring 352.3 feet.

Then in the summer of 1966 a 385-foot tree was discovered in the Redwood Creek region by Rudolph W. Becking, a forest research consultant. With one leap the record for tree height was extended an astonishing 18 feet.

Will it end there? Or will the legendary 400-foot tree come to light eventually? Is there any limit at all on the height a tree can grow?

Galileo, the great Italian astronomer of four centuries ago, would not have believed in 300-foot trees. "An oak 200 cubits [300 feet] high," he wrote, "would not be able to sustain its own branches if they were distributed as in a tree of ordinary size." What he meant by that, it seems, is that a tree so huge could not possibly pump enough sap to its upper boughs to nourish them. In Europe, where a tree 100 feet tall is considered unusually large, Galileo's theory may have seemed convincing; but we have the evidence of Redwood Creek Valley to show that even at heights of 360 to 385 feet trees can carry sap to their uppermost levels. As Paul A. Zahl explains:

> Modern plant physiologists know that the vertical movement of sap is due mainly to the extraordinary cohesive properties of the water molecule: As the molecule moves, it tugs its neighbors along.
> Within the wood's sap tissues, water-filled capillaries extend from the lowest rootlets to the highest foliage. The capillaries end there in minute openings on the surface of leaf or needle, where water constantly evaporates. As one molecule vaporizes, another replaces it from below; in other words, because of the forces of molecular cohesion, the entire water column moves upward by the volume of one molecule. If trillions of molecules evaporate, as in fact they do, the water column rises correspondingly.

When the height record for trees was 350 feet, there was no theoretical reason why a 360-foot tree could not someday be found, and in time a number of them were. From 360 feet to 385 feet is a big increase in feet, but the overall increase in tree size is only about 7 percent. It seems reasonable that a tree might rise a mere 5 percent above the current record holder—thus topping 400 feet. If so, could not a tree rise 5 percent above that one, and then another rise and then another, until redwoods reached to the moon?

We know that there are no trees as tall as a thousand feet, not even in some secluded grove of *Sequoia sempervirens*. It is doubtful that the redwoods can even attain a height of 500 feet. A few 400-foot trees may be scattered through the California forests, but this height appears to be the physical limit for the redwoods. The difficulty lies in the nature of wood itself. If redwoods grew ribs of steel, they might top the Empire State Building; but there are no thousand-foot redwoods for the same reason that there are no wooden skyscrapers. The taller a structure is, the more support it requires. Without the reinforcement of steel or concrete, a super-redwood would need a trunk as thick as a city block to support it. Since air currents are turbulent high above the ground, it would also require an enormous root system to hold it erect. It appears biologically impossible for a redwood to develop the necessary huge base and sprawling anchor of roots. Throughout its lifetime a redwood's growth continues, but at an extremely slow rate once it has risen 300 feet. It may ultimately near the 400-foot level, but further growth would be slight.

Sequoia sempervirens is not likely to be challenged for its height records by its cousin of the Sierra Nevada. For one thing, *Sequoia gigantea* is so scarce that few if any of the great trees are undiscovered, whereas there are still thousands of unexplored acres of redwood forest; for another, the giant sequoia runs more to bulk than it does to height.

It *is* an extremely tall tree, but many other species exceed it. On the average, the giant sequoia reaches heights of about 250 feet, and the tallest known living specimen stands 310 feet high. Two fallen trees in the Giant Forest of Sequoia National Park measured 318 and 319 feet, and another fallen tree in the Redwood Mountain Grove (misnamed, for there are no coast redwoods there) of Kings Canyon National Park stretched 347 feet. With these few exceptions, the giant sequoia is outscaled by any number of redwoods, by numerous Australian eucalyptus trees, and by the tallest Douglas firs; two other trees of the Pacific Northwest, the Sitka spruce and the western hemlock, come close to equaling the giant sequoia in average height.

But *Sequoia gigantea* surpasses all other living things in bulk. It is so much larger in overall dimensions than other trees that the extent of its massiveness is hard to comprehend. And nothing in the animal kingdom comes close to equaling its immensity. The blue whale, bulkiest of all past or present animals (including the dinosaurs), may reach a weight of about 150 tons. Even an unremarkable giant sequoia weighs *twenty times* as much—3,000 tons. The great thickness of the trees gives them extraordinary mass.

The tallest redwoods we know—those in Redwood Creek Valley—are 12 to 15 feet thick at ground level. Since the circumference of a tree is normally a little over three times its diameter, these trees range from 40 to 50 feet in circumference at their bases, and taper rapidly to much more slender dimensions above. The thickest redwoods (which do not happen to be the tallest) have diameters of under 23 feet; most redwoods are less than half as thick. Other trees that grow to 250 feet or more, such as the Douglas fir or the eucalyptus, are even slimmer in base circumference.

But there are hundreds of giant sequoias that are 25 feet thick or more at the base, and a good many that exceed 30 feet. This is greater than the distance from wall to wall in most classrooms. At ground level the trunks of these trees, gnarled and spreading, thick-barked and rough, seem alien and strange; it is hard to believe that they are trees at all, they are so wide and massive. The thickest of all is the General Grant Tree in Grant Grove, Kings Canyon National Park; its base diameter is 40.3 feet, its circumference 107.6 feet, and it stands 267.4 feet tall.

The acme of immensity, though, is the General Sherman Tree in the Giant Forest of Sequoia National Park. At 272.4 feet, General Sherman is slightly taller than General Grant; it would probably be much taller if lightning had not lopped

away much of its crown centuries ago. General Sherman is slightly slimmer in the waist than General Grant, having a base diameter of a mere 37 feet and a circumference of 101.6 feet; but the overall bulk of the General Sherman Tree is greater than that of the General Grant because the taper of General Sherman's trunk is more gradual. At a height of 60 feet, General Sherman's trunk is 17.5 feet thick while General Grant measures 16.3 feet; 120 feet above the ground, Sherman is still 17 feet thick, but Grant is only 15 feet. As these figures show, once a giant sequoia has risen a short distance from its spread-out base, it ascends almost as a straight cylinder for more than the full height of most other trees before it begins to taper.

Other trees sometimes are put forth as rivals to the giant sequoias in bulk. The baobab tree of Africa attains a trunk diameter of 30 feet at the base, but its height is nowhere near that of *gigantea*. At Tule, near Oaxaca, Mexico, there is a Mexican cypress—a distant relative of the sequoias— that is 36.1 feet in diameter and has a circumference of 162 feet. This is thicker than any giant sequoia, but the Tule tree is thought by most botanists to be a freak, several trees whose trunks have grown together. It is only 130 feet tall.

The height and width of the giant sequoias combine to give them immense total bulk. The General Sherman Tree is estimated to weigh more than 6,100 tons, and to have a volume of nearly 50,000 cubic feet, exclusive of limbs. There is enough wood in the General Sherman to build 40 five-room houses; and if a tunnel similar to that in the former Wawona Tree were cut through the lower trunk, three cars abreast could drive through it at once without fear of a scratched fender! One of its branches alone is larger than

The largest living giant sequoia is the General Sherman Tree.

most of the trees in the United States. This phenomenal branch begins 130 feet off the ground, where it has a diameter of 6.8 feet; and its length exceeds 150 feet.

No one is going to build five-room houses out of the General Sherman, or to cut any tunnels through its base. Nearly all of the giant sequoias—unlike the redwoods—are now in state or national parks and are carefully protected. In the nineteenth century, though, when these trees were still being logged, they produced some startling statistics. The geographer Ellsworth Huntington, an early student of the sequoias, wrote that "3,000 fence posts, sufficient to support a wire fence around 8,000 or 9,000 acres, have been made from one of these giants, and that was only the first step towards using its carcass. 650,000 shingles, enough to cover the roofs of 70 or 80 houses, formed the second item of its product; finally there still remained hundreds of cords of firewood which no one could use because of the prohibitive cost of hauling the wood out of the mountains."

The age of the giant sequoias and the redwoods has also long been a matter for astonishment. In the nineteenth century it was customary to say that both trees reached ages of 4,000 years or more, but these estimates were based more on enthusiasm than on study. Since the only reliable way to discover the age of a tree is to cut it down and count the growth rings, a considerable body of information about their ages was accumulated as the redwoods and giant sequoias began to fall to the timbermen.

The oldest redwoods seem to be about 2,200 years of age. Standing before one of these trees, we have to persuade ourselves somehow that it sprouted from its seed around the time Hannibal was threatening Rome; that it was a majestic giant when Christ was born; that it was ancient in the days of Charlemagne; that it was celebrating its 1,700th birthday

BEGAN
GROWING
650 A.D.

600

700

800

900

1000

1100

1200

1300

1400

1500

1600

1700

A.D.

A tree's age is determined by counting its growth rings. This giant sequoia, felled in 1891, was over 1300 years old.

as Columbus set sail; that it has lived on through storm and danger into the era of space travel and atomic power. In the lifetime of such a tree, only a brief interlude of time separates George Washington from John F. Kennedy; the arrival of the Pilgrim Fathers seems a recent event; William the Conqueror's defeat of the English in 1066 happened less than half its life-span ago. Yet this venerable redwood is only a youngster compared with most giant sequoias.

The nineteenth-century naturalist John Muir, patiently examining fallen trees in what is now Sequoia National Forest, California, found many giant sequoias with 3,000 growth rings or more. "On one of the Kings River giants, thirty-five feet and eight inches in diameter, exclusive of bark," Muir wrote, "I counted upwards of four thousand annual wood rings, in which there was no decay after all these centuries of mountain weather." No one has ever been able to find Muir's 4,000-year-old tree, but he was an honest man and a reliable one, and we can assume he was telling the truth. Certainly there is no shortage of giant sequoias whose stumps show 3,000 rings or more; many have 3,200–3,500 rings. It seems likely that the normal life-span of these trees is a *minimum* of three thousand years.

Many trees have been said to equal or surpass the giant sequoia in age. Various estimates place the great cypress at Tule, Mexico, between 2,000 to 5,000 years of age; there is no way of knowing without cutting down the tree, but a figure of 3,000 years is accepted even by conservative authorities. A cypress in Chapultepec Park in Mexico City is supposedly 6,000 years old, but again there is no proof. The banyan tree of India and the baobab of Africa are thought to live at least 3,000 years, and a famous dragon tree (*Dracaena draco*) that grew on Tenerife in the Canary Islands was believed to be nearly twice that age when it was blown down by a storm in 1868.

Only one tree, however, is definitely known to exceed the giant sequoia in length of life. In 1953 the title of "oldest living thing" passed without dispute from the noble giant sequoia to the weird, gnarled bristlecone pine (*Pinus aristata*) of California's White Mountains. Here, in Inyo National Forest, the bristlecones grow at altitudes of 10,000 to 12,000 feet under harsh conditions that no other trees can tolerate. They receive less than 10 inches of rain a year; the wind flails them mercilessly; they are whipped by sleet and sand that strip away bark and leaves. Squat, growing close to the ground, twisting themselves into grotesque knots, the bristlecones are polished by the elements to a sandy gray sheen, so that they look like driftwood.

Living driftwood, though. Dr. Edmund Schulman of the

University of Arizona was able to find seventeen bristle-cones that were more than 4,000 years old; one, nicknamed Methuselah, has attained an age of 4,600 years. It was possible to determine the ages of the bristlecones by taking cores of wood from their trunks and counting the growth rings; this cannot be done with the giant sequoias or red-woods because of the great size of the trunks, but bristle-cones are not large trees. The biggest one has a circumfer-ence of 36 feet 8 inches, which is respectable enough as trees go, but far short of sequoia girth; and most of the bristle-cones are much smaller. From these cores Dr. Schulman was able to show that the bristlecone pine lives a thousand years or more longer than the longest-lived giant sequoias.

But it is a kind of death-in-life. The bristlecone dies by inches, one limb after another giving up life while one stub-born part of the tree hangs on. Pine Alpha, a 4,300-year-old bristlecone, is 90-percent dead; most of it is lifeless wood, with just a narrow 10-inch strip of bark and living sapwood remaining. Yet Pine Alpha still produces seeds from which new trees can sprout. Most of the other bristlecones likewise sustain life in only a small section of the total tree, and the forest where they grow has a forlorn, barren look, seemingly a forest of the living dead.

The giant sequoia, on the other hand, remains in full vigor throughout the thirty or thirty-five centuries of its life-span. "Nothing hurts the Big Tree," John Muir wrote. "I never saw one that was sick or showed the slightest sign of decay. It lives on through indefinite thousands of years, until burned, blown down, undermined, or shattered by some tre-mendous lightning stroke."

Both species of sequoia do seem immune to most of the plagues that bedevil lesser trees. Neither insects nor parasitic fungi can harm them. Certain insects such as the sequoia bark beetle and the sequoia scale burrow in them or attack their foliage, but without serious effects.

Like the redwood, the giant sequoia suffers no serious threat from fire, the enemy of most trees. Both species have thick, asbestoslike bark—often more than a foot thick—which will not burn readily even under intense heat, and which shields the tree's living tissues within. Though forest fires kill young sequoias, those only a century or two old and net yet able to withstand the blaze, the real titans survive. The flames that lick about them, turning underbrush to ashes and charcoal, are unable to destroy them.

There is a strange beauty in these fires. John Muir, whose love of the big trees drew him to them even when flames roared through the forests, wrote this magnificent description of a fire in what now is Kings Canyon National Park:

> In the forest between the Middle and East Fork of Kaweah River I met a grand fire; and as fire is the master scourge and controller of the distribution of trees, I stopped to watch it and learn what I could of its works and ways with the giants. It came racing up the steep chaparral-covered slopes of the East Fork canyon with passionate enthusiasm in a broad cataract of flames: now bending down low to feed on the green bushes, devouring acres of them at a breath; now towering high in the air, as if looking abroad to choose a way; then stopping to feed again, the lurid flapping surges and the smoke and terrible rushing and roaring hiding all that is gentle and orderly in the work. But as soon as the deep forest was reached the ungovernable flood became calm, like a torrent entering a lake, creeping and spreading beneath the trees where the ground was level or sloped gently, slowly nibbling the cake of compressed needles and scales with flames an inch high, rising here and there to a foot or two on dry twigs and clumps of small bushes and brome grass. Only at considerable intervals were fierce bon-

fires lighted, where heavy branches broken off by snow had accumulated, or around some venerable giant whose head had been stricken off by lightning.

I tethered Brownie on the edge of a little meadow beside a stream, a good safe way off, and then cautiously chose a camp for myself in a big stout hollow trunk, not likely to be crushed by the fall of burning trees, and made a bed of ferns and boughs in it. The night, however, and the strange wild fireworks were too beautiful and exciting to allow much sleep. There was no danger of being chased and hemmed in; for in the main forest belt of the Sierra, even when swift winds are blowing, fires seldom or never sweep over the trees in broad all-embracing sheets, as they do in the dense Rocky Mountain woods and in those of the Cascade Mountains of Oregon and Washington. Here they creep from tree to tree with tranquil deliberation, allowing close observation, though caution is required in venturing around the burning giants, to avoid falling limbs and knots and fragments from dead shattered tops. Though the day was best for study, I sauntered about night after night, learning what I could and admiring the wonderful show vividly displayed in the lonely darkness: the ground fire advancing in long crooked lines, gently grazing and smoking on the close-pressed leaves, springing up in thousands of little jets of pure flame on dry tassels and twigs, and tall spires and flat sheets with jagged flapping edges dancing here and there on grass tufts and bushes; big bonfires blazing in perfect storms of energy, where heavy branches mixed with small ones lay smashed together in hundred-cord piles; big red arches between spreading root swells and trees growing close together; huge fire-mantled trunks on the hill slopes glowing like bars of hot iron; violet-colored fire running up the tall trees, tracing the furrows of the bark in quick quivering rills, and lighting magnificent torches on dry shattered tops; and ever and anon, with a tremendous roar and burst of light, young trees clad in low-descending feathery branches vanishing in one flame two or three hundred feet high.

One of the most impressive and beautiful sights was made by the great fallen trunks lying on the hillsides, all red and glowing like colossal iron bars fresh from a furnace, two hundred feet long, some of them, and ten to twenty feet thick. After repeated burnings have consumed the bark and sapwood, the sound charred surface, being full of cracks and sprinkled with leaves, is quickly overspread with a pure rich furred ruby glow, almost flameless and smokeless, producing a marvelous effect in the night. Another grand and interesting sight are the fires on the tops of the largest living trees, flaming above the green branches at a height of perhaps two hundred feet, entirely cut off from the ground fires, and looking like signal beacons on watch towers. From one standpoint I sometimes saw a dozen or more, those in the distance looking like great stars above the forest roof. At first I could not imagine how these Sequoia lamps were lighted, but the very first night, strolling about, waiting and watching, I saw the thing done again and again. The thick fibrous bark of old trees is divided by deep, nearly continuous furrows, the sides of which are bearded with the bristling ends of fibers broken by the growth swelling of the trunk; and when the fire comes creeping around the foot of the tree, it runs up these bristly furrows in lovely pale blue quivering, bickering rills of flame, with a low, earnest, whispering sound, to the lightning-shattered top of the trunk, which, in the dry Indian summer, with perhaps leaves and twigs and squirrel-gnawed cone scales and seed wings lodged on it, is readily ignited. These lamp-lighting rills, the most beautiful fire streams I ever saw, last only a minute or two; but the big lamps burn with varying brightness for days and weeks, throwing off sparks like the spray of a fountain, while ever and anon a shower of red coals comes sifting down through the branches, followed at times, with startling effect, by a burned-off chunk weighing perhaps half a ton.

Such forest fires may reach temperatures of 3,000 or 4,000 degrees. The bark of the great trees turns red, then

The tunneled-out Wawona Tree was impressive testimony of the giant sequoia's determination to survive. It stood from 1881 to April, 1969.

incandescent white in the furious heat, and the cambium, the living, growing sapwood just beneath the bark, will be killed over a large area of the base. Later, the bark will crack and fall off where the cambium has died, exposing the dead sapwood beneath and making the tree more vulnerable to the next fire. Even so, the tree endures fire after fire, remaining alive though its trunk bears many terrible scars. The healing power of the sequoia is one of its most remarkable features. A fire may leave a redwood or a giant sequoia bearing a wound 3 yards wide and 20 feet high gouged deeply into the trunk; and yet, as soon as the fire is out, the tree begins the slow task of closing the gaping wound. Year after year, the bark inches back over the charred area, until after a century or more the outer surface of the tree once more is whole.

The amount of damage sequoias can endure without dying is hard to believe. Yosemite Park's Wawona Tree lived for 88 years after a huge tunnel was cut through its base, until it simply toppled over in April, 1969. Many trees of both species have suffered far more ghastly wounds and still live; the entire core of the trunk may have been burned out, so that one can step inside and look up through the shell as though it were a colossal chimney, and yet there will be a few living branches high above. Mere charred snags, grim and gaunt, cling to life in the forests; nothing on earth matches the determination of these trees to survive.

Scientists have traced the record of this amazing vitality as it is written in the growth rings of felled trees. The biography of one giant sequoia that was cut down in 1900 showed that its first encounter with fire came in A.D. 245, when it was a mere 516 years old. A forest blaze at that time left a scar that took 105 years to heal. For twelve centuries the tree was untouched; but in the year 1441, when it was 1,712 years of age, another fire left two long grooves on its sides, one foot and two feet wide respectively, which required close to a century to heal. In 1580, at the age of 1,851, the tree again suffered a long burn two feet wide, and needed 56 years to cover it with new tissue. The next fire, in 1797, must have been a savage holocaust, for the 2,068-year-old tree received a scar 18 feet in width. Over the next 103 years, it succeeded in reducing the exposed area of the burn to about 14 feet; but then came the saws of lumbermen, enemies far more deadly than fire, and the ancient tree fell.

A fire-damaged sequoia, in danger of toppling, tries to heal itself by growing a buttress to support the leaning trunk.

Repeatedly closing its wounds, hiding the charred wood beneath clean new growth, a sequoia can hold fast against a fire of almost any intensity, increasing in bulk and height every year. But its weakness lies hidden: its roots.

Unlike most trees, sequoias do not have deep taproots that lock them to the earth; their roots are widespread but shallow. A severe fire in the underbrush can kill great sections of a tree's roots, weakening the tree's ability to take in nourishment and disturbing its balance. Sequoias can replace fire-killed roots again and again, but sometimes a tree begins to lean in the direction of the damage, tipping forward precariously until its crown is 40 feet or more out of line with its base. The tree will try to heal itself, by growing a strong supporting buttress which will prop up the trunk on the side where the roots have been killed. But the growth of a buttress is slow—at best, half an inch a year—and the tree may be off balance for decades.

This is the chief vulnerability of these forest monarchs. When fire has damaged the roots of a sequoia, or stream erosion has cut away supporting soil on one side of its base, the tree may begin to lean. Then, although it is as healthy and strong as before, a gust of wind may prove too strong, or a flood may leave the ground too soggy. The roots will no longer to be able to hold, and the tree will fall.

For a giant sequoia this is death; but a fallen redwood refuses to die. If the severed roots of a toppled tree remain in the ground, dozens of new saplings will rise. A cut stump will also send up sprouts. Most astonishingly, new redwoods will spring from a broken-off trunk, growing from wartlike swellings called burls that cluster near a redwood's base, and sprout into life when the parent tree dies. (Every year, thousands of tourists buy small burls, from which tiny redwood trees will grow if the burls are placed in water.) The hordes of little trees which rise on the site where their ancestor once towered put down roots of their own and compete for space in the forest. Most will perish, but the strongest endure and rapidly grow upward. In the redwood forests one can often find four or five trees of great size growing in a narrow circle, the daughter trees that sprouted long ago from some fallen titan.

Close relatives though they are, the redwood and the sequoia differ in many respects besides height, thickness and life-span. They are also unlike one another in habitat, foliage, size of cones, and other features.

The redwood requires plenty of moisture and demands a climate that is never very hot or very cold. In the United States, only the cool, rainy, fogbound strip of Pacific Coast from southern Oregon to northern California has the right environment for it. The southernmost limits of its range lie in the Santa Lucia Mountains along the California shore below Carmel; and here, because the climate is fairly dry and warm, the redwoods grow sparsely, keeping to deep narrow canyons where shade, streams, and underground springs make up for the lack of rain. To the north, above San Francisco, the redwood stands become thicker, wherever the spread of civilization has permitted the trees to survive at all. The grandest forests are found in California's two huge and thinly populated northern counties, Humboldt and Del Norte, where the rainfall measures 50 to 100 inches a year. Here, as a million years ago, dense groves of mighty redwoods still exist, and trees reach heights of 350 feet. Across the border in Oregon, the stands gradually thin out again as the climate becomes colder.

Although this coastal empire is narrow, only 10 to 40 miles wide, a virtually continuous belt of redwoods is maintained for nearly 500 miles. And so the redwood is not a rare tree; even after a century of heavy logging, some 300,000 acres of redwoods remain, of the 2,000,000 virgin acres that grew before the white man came. (Of the remaining trees, though, only about 70,000 acres are preserved in public parks and groves, and most of the rest will probably be logged before the end of this century.)

The giant sequoia, on the other hand, is a rare tree indeed—among the most limited in range and number of individuals of any important tree species. It occurs singly or in small groups, at altitudes of 4,000 to 8,000 feet, along the western slopes of the Sierra Nevada Mountains. Within this strip, about 250 miles long, there are about seventy-two separate groves, some with only half a dozen trees and others containing thousands. The total area occupied by all of these groves is less than 15,000 acres. There are probably fewer than 20,000 giant sequoias in the world with diameters greater than 10 feet; fortunately, nearly all of these are in public hands.

The leaves of the redwood are short flat needles, a little less than an inch in length and about an eighth of an inch wide, arranged in a double row; they look much like the familiar needles of Eastern hemlocks or firs. The giant sequoia's leaves are quite different: small overlapping scale-like needles resembling those of the juniper. Most evergreens lose only a few needles at a time, but sequoias shed an entire twig or spray at once. Each spray lives three or four years and then falls from the tree; but the shedding is done in rotation, so that the tree always is covered with leaves.

If you wish to see the leaves of a redwood or a giant sequoia, you must look at these fallen sprays or at the branches of a very young tree, for a mature tree has no foliage within easy reach. Young sequoias have branches all the way to the

Leaves and cones of the giant sequoia. The cones are usually only two or three inches long.

ground, giving them the triangular look of Christmas trees; but as the trees grow, the lower branches die and fall away. A full-grown tree may have no branches for the first 150 feet of its height; giant sequoias, in particular, develop an oddly bare look in old age, having an immense naked trunk topped by a distant and tiny crown of green.

The cones of both trees are found only in the lofty upper branches. The redwood's cones are curiously small, less than an inch long. Those of the giant sequoia are bigger, but not really large—two to three inches in length. Sealed under the hard scales of these cones are small seeds, two to six of them beneath each scale. The seeds are astonishingly little: the giant sequoia, mightiest of living things, sprouts from a seed that weighs just one five-thousandth of an ounce!

Each fall and winter some of the cones open, releasing the winged seeds, which drift on the wind for great distances.

VANISHING GIANTS

John Muir wrote:

> The faint lisp of snowflakes as they alight is one of the smallest sounds mortal can hear. The sound of falling Sequoia seeds, even when they happen to strike on flat leaves or flakes of bark, is about as faint. Very different are the bumping and thudding of the falling cones. Most of them are cut off by the Douglas squirrel, and stored for the sake of the seeds, small as they are. In the calm Indian summer these busy harvesters with ivory sickles go to work early in the morning, as soon as breakfast is over, and nearly all day the ripe cones fall in a steady pattering, bumping shower. Unless harvested in this way, they discharge their seeds, and remain on the tree for many years. In fruitful seasons the trees are fairly laden. On small specimen branches, one and a half and two inches in diameter, I counted four hundred and eighty cones. No other California conifer produces nearly so many seeds, excepting perhaps its relative, the redwood of the Coast Mountains. Millions are ripened annually by a single tree, and the product of one of the main groves in a fruitful year would suffice to plant all the mountain ranges of the world.

Most of these millions of seeds land in places where they are unable to take root, or are devoured by hungry squirrels. Others are sterile. Fertile seeds that do find favorable conditions when they alight send down tiny roots, send up the first tender shoots, and rapidly begin their conquest of the forest's upper levels. The seedlings rise swiftly, competing with one another to reach the sunlight. Many of them perish early in the darkness of the forest floor; only a few have the vigor needed to survive. Those that do survive are soon slender, fairly tall saplings, unremarkable in appearance. Depending on conditions of soil and moisture, they may add anywhere from eight inches to a foot to their height each year. A fraction of an inch is the annual gain in the width of the trunk. After a century or so, the tree is as big as a good-sized

Eastern evergreen—say, 100 feet tall and 3 or 4 feet in diameter. But the Eastern tree has reached maturity; the sequoia is just beginning to grow.

The redwood becomes thicker as it grows taller; by its 400th birthday it may top the 200-foot mark. Thereafter, growth is slower, but still steady. It loses its lower branches. Perhaps it bears the scars of several fires. When it passes its 1,000th birthday, still young, still rising, it nears a height of 300 feet. And still it grows.

The giant sequoia follows the same pattern, though it does not remain as slender as the redwood. The rate at which it broadens differs greatly according to growing conditions. John Muir reported that "a tree about ten feet in diameter that grew on the side of a meadow was, according to my own count of the wood rings, only two hundred and fifty-nine years old at the time it was felled, while another in the same grove, of almost exactly the same size, but less favorably situated, was fourteen hundred and forty years old. The Calaveras tree cut for a dance floor was twenty-four [actually twenty-seven] feet in diameter, and only thirteen hundred years old; another, about the same size, was a thousand years older."

As it reaches its maximum height of 250 to 300 feet, the giant sequoia loses the last remnants of its early grace. Its lower branches are gone; but tremendous upper branches, each the size of an ordinary tree, give its crown a rounded, dome-shaped look. The bark thickens, with large gnarled buttresses forming at the base of the trunk. The color of the bark becomes a light, bright reddish brown, whereas younger trees are darker, almost tinged with purple. The tree has reached maturity. And there it will stand, through the next fifteen or twenty or thirty centuries, gigantic, seemingly eternal, alone in its strange grandeur.

VI
The Big Trees on Show

When the giant sequoias of the Sierra Nevada became generally known, soon after A. T. Dowd came upon the Calaveras Grove in 1852, they stirred great excitement. In short order various Californians were devising projects to exploit the trees as tourist attractions.

The first endeavor along this line was innocent enough. A man named William W. Lapham acquired the rights to Dowd's discovery site, built a cabin there, and set himself up in business as a guide to the grove. Visitors came—at first only a few brave travelers, then hordes of the curious. In 1856 Lapham sold out to James Sperry, who built a hotel at Murphy's Camp that offered lodgings to tourists until it was destroyed by fire in 1943. It became customary for visitors to California to come out from San Francisco, spend a night at the ramshackle hotel in Murphy's Camp, and go on for a look at the Calaveras Grove; kings and dukes, presidents and prime ministers, financiers and congressmen, all came and gazed in astonishment upon these botanical marvels.

Only the very rich, though, could afford to travel to

far-off California merely to behold trees. How much more profitable it would be to chop one of the big trees down and ship it east to be placed on public exhibition! Many thousands of people, instead of only a few hundred, would be able to see the biggest of all living things—and the same tree could be hauled all over the country to be shown again and again.

In the summer of 1853 a group of Californians set out to make this idea a reality. Under the leadership of Captain W. H. Hanford of Murphy Camp's Union Water Company, they picked one of the noblest of the Calaveras titans—a tree more than 300 feet high and close to 100 feet in circumference at ground level—and arranged to have it cut down.

Easy to arrange, not so easy to do. The loggers went to work with their saws and axes, but the size of the tree made a mockery of their efforts. Days of hacking and cutting failed to accomplish anything. A special method of logging had to be devised: five men were equipped with huge drills called pump augers with which they bored holes through the bark toward the center of the tree. After twenty-two days they had ringed the tree completely with holes, so that the trunk was virtually severed from its base. Still the mighty tree stood upright. The loggers hammered wedges into the trunk, in the hope of forcing the tree to fall—and fall it did, but before the loggers were ready to have it come down. A gust of wind swept through the sequoia's crown and tipped it. Four million pounds of tree slammed into the earth with a crash that could be felt thousands of feet away. The great branches broke into kindling and the colossal trunk split into many immense sections that were buried deep in the ground by the force of their own fall. It was, one observer said, a "botanical tragedy."

Loggers worked from platforms built around the trunk, several feet above the ground.

There was no way to put the shattered tree together for exhibition. Captain Hanford and his fellow promoters had to content themselves with collecting the bark from the thickest part of the tree and patching the pieces into something that would give an idea of how the living tree had looked. A magazine called *Gleason's Pictorial* offered this somber appraisal of the shabby enterprise in its issue of October 1, 1853:

> Probably it will not be very long before our readers will be able to get a view of this monster of the California woods for a trifling admission fee. In Europe such a natural production would have been cherished and protected, if necessary by law; but in this money-making, go-ahead community, 30 or 40 thousand dollars are paid for it, and the purchaser chops it down and ships it off for a shilling show.
>
> In its natural condition, rearing its majestic head towards heaven, and waving in all its native vigor, strength, and

verdure, it was a sight worth a pilgrimage to see; but now alas, it is only a monument to the cupidity of those who have destroyed all there was of interest connected with it.

The bark was assembled in San Francisco late in 1853. Among those who viewed it was the English botanist William Lobb, who had come to America to collect unusual plants for a botanical garden at Chelsea, England. Lobb's account of the big tree, which appeared in the *Illustrated London News* for February 11, 1854, declared:

> Of this vegetable monster 21 feet of the bark from the lower part of the trunk have been put in the natural form in San Francisco for exhibition; it there forms a spacious carpeted room, and contains a piano with seats for 40 persons. On one occasion 140 children were admitted without inconvenience.

Captain Hanford and his partners arranged for additional strips of the tree's bark to be added to the original 21 feet, more than doubling the height of the mutilated sequoia. They also had loggers saw a section of the wood from side to side, to give an idea of the interior of the tree. The stump itself, which remained in the ground, was cleared of debris, cut smooth, and polished to make a dance floor; at a height of six feet above the ground it had a diameter of 27 feet. James M. Hutchings, who visited it on July 4, 1854, wrote, "However incredible it may appear . . . the writer formed one of a cotillion party of 32 persons dancing upon this stump, in addition to which the musicians and lookers-on numbered 17, making a total of 49 occupants on its surface at one time."

By then the bark had traveled far from the forest where the murdered tree had grown for an estimated 1,300 years. Following its exhibition in San Francisco, it had been shipped via Cape Horn to New York City, where Captain Hanford had arranged for it to go on show in the spring of 1854. This advertisement appeared in the New York *Herald* on April 29, 1854:

> The big tree, from California—ready for exhibition on the 8th of May. The immense tree recently felled upon the Sierra Nevada, California, has at length arrived in the city of New York, where it is placed for public exhibition in the spacious Racket Court, adjoining the Metropolitan Hotel, Broadway. This gigantic monarch of the forest measured, while standing, three hundred and twenty feet in height, and ninety five feet in circumference. Its age has been estimated at three thousand years [a considerable exaggeration]. . . . The tree was felled by means of large pump augers, requiring the labor of ten men for twenty-six days [also exaggerations], at an expense of five hundred dollars, besides the immense cost of removing it on ship board, and transporting it hither. This is the same tree described in a February number of the London Illustrated News, Gleason's Pictorial, of October and March last, and noticed by several of the leading journalists. It was likewise seen standing in its natural state by Senator Gwin, Mr. Adams, of the Express Company, and several other gentlemen, whose certificates will vouch for its identity. This is the first time it has ever been offered for exhibition since it left San Francisco. The bark was stripped from the tree for the length of fifty feet from the base, and is from one to two feet in thickness. It was taken off in sections, so that it can be placed, relatively, in its original position, and thus give the beholder a just idea of the gigantic dimensions of the tree. So placed, it occupies a space of about thirty feet in diameter, or ninety feet in circumference, and fifty feet in height. A piece of wood will be shown which has been cut from the tree across the whole diameter.

Hanford soon realized that he had made a serious error

in planning to begin showing his tree on May 8. That was only four days after the scheduled reopening of New York's gaudy exhibition hall, the Crystal Palace, under the new management of the famous showman, P. T. Barnum. The Crystal Palace was a huge, rambling structure of glass and metal that had been erected in Bryant Park on 42nd Street, next to the Croton Reservoir, where the New York Public Library now stands. Intended as a kind of World's Fair under one roof, the Crystal Palace had found itself in trouble almost from the moment it was conceived, and its first season, which lasted for three months in 1853, had been a financial disaster. Faced with bankruptcy, the directors of the Crystal Palace called in Barnum to run the second season, hoping that his talents for publicity and entertainment

The stump of a giant sequoia. In addition to the usual saws and axes, loggers used wedges like those in the center of the stump to cut down the big trees.

would rouse public interest. Barnum stirred up so much excitement over the opening of the new season that Hanford saw it would be hopeless to open a competing attraction the same week. He kept his big tree under wraps all through the month of May. When he opened it to the public in June, the public failed to come. Hanford stored the bark in a warehouse, and not long afterward the warehouse caught fire, bringing Hanford's fiasco to its end.

This dismal experience did not prevent another promoter, George L. Trask, from trying to capitalize on the grandeur of the giant sequoias. In the summer of 1854 Trask selected as his victim an even more spectacular example of the species from the Calaveras Grove. This was a tree that the Indians called "the Mother of the Forest." It stood 321 feet in height and was about 90 feet in circumference.

Remembering the difficulties that Hanford had experienced in cutting his tree down, and the catastrophic way in which the tree had eventually fallen, Trask devised a far more hideous fate for the Mother of the Forest. He would not bother to fell the tree at all. Instead he would merely erect a scaffold and peel the bark from the living tree to a point just below the first branches, which would expose the sapwood and eventually kill the tree. The bark could be carted off as a touring exhibition, while the stripped Mother of the Forest was left to meet a slow death in her native grove.

Ladders and rope slings went up, auger holes were driven into the trunk, and rungs were inserted in the holes so that the workmen could scramble to their tasks. Plate by plate, the thick bark was cut loose, to a height of 116 feet. The numbered sections, each 8 feet long, were taken down and hauled off to Stockton, California, where they were packed for shipping around Cape Horn to New York. Debarked, despoiled, the Mother of the Forest remained in her place, a grim symbol of man's greed. For any common tree it will be fatal within a couple of years to remove a ring of bark that goes completely around the trunk, even if that ring is only a few inches wide. But this giant sequoia lived on for a full generation, struggling to adapt to its terrible wound. It was still living in 1878 when a Scottish traveler, Constance Frederica Gordon Cumming, visited the grove. She compared the tree to the early Christian martyr who lived for days while Roman archers filled his body with arrows. She wrote, "I can see her [the Mother of the Forest] from where I now sit—a ghastly object—her sides still transfixed with wooden implements of torture—the St. Sebastian of the forest."

The first destination for the bark of the Mother of the Forest was none other than the Crystal Palace. Barnum's wizardry had failed to raise the exhibition hall's attendance figures after all; when the second season closed, bankruptcy was threatening again, and shortly Barnum resigned. Word circulated that the Palace would close permanently. But Horace Greeley of the New York *Tribune* took charge of the hall and declared that it would open for yet another season.

It did open in the spring of 1855, but many of its best exhibits had been removed by their owners. *The New York Times* commented sourly that "the interior of the Crystal Palace is fast becoming a beggarly array of empty space." A few weeks later the bark of the Mother of the Forest, an exhibit capable of filling most of that empty space, arrived.

On July 3, the New York City newspapers published this advertisement (complete with the customary exaggerations of the big tree's size, as though it needed to have a fictitious 40 feet of height bestowed on it):

VANISHING GIANTS

THE TREE MASTODON: A Mountain of wood—a single tree taller by a hundred feet than the Bunker Hill monument. Great attraction at the Crystal Palace—The Monarch of the California Forest, supposed to be the largest tree in the world, has arrived at this port from San Francisco, and will be exhibited in the Crystal Palace, the only building in New York large enough to contain it on and after the

FOURTH OF JULY

The giant tree has been named by botanists, *Washingtonia gigantea.* It measured when standing 363 feet from base to summit. Its diameter is 31 feet at the base and 15½ feet at the distance of 116 feet from the roots. No big tree ever exhibited and none of its race remaining in California compare with this Sylvan Mastodon, or as it was called by the California Indians in their language the "Mother of the Forest." The Crystal Palace has been rented at a vast expense for the exhibition, which transcends in interest all the marvels for which California is celebrated. Doors open 8 A.M. until 8 P.M. Admission is 25 cents. N. B. Hayward's splendid Quadrille Band will be in attendance.

Trask's exhibit was more than twice as high as the one Hanford had sent east the year before, and so it looked more like a section of a colossal tree and less like some incomprehensible wooden mass. The citizens of New York hastened to see the botanical wonder. An advertisement in the *Tribune* on July 6 claimed that "this enormous sample of the 'Tall Timber' of California attracted upwards of six thousand persons on the Fourth of July," adding quite accurately, "This phenomenon of the vegetable kingdom is creating as much astonishment among scientific men as among the community at large." An ad in the *Times* four days later boasted grandly if incorrectly that the living tree's height had been "equal to that of the third Pyramid of the Nile." (That pyramid is actually only 204 feet high.) In a news article, the New York *Evening Post* observed on July 7 that "all 'big-trees' heretofore exhibited were pigmies to this tower of timber," while an article in the *Evening Express* compared the tree favorably to Hanford's 50-foot specimen.

By way of lending a touch of authenticity, Trask published an affidavit from a witness of high reputation who asserted that it was indeed the case that 60 tons of bark, covering a height of 116 feet, had been stripped from a single California tree. The witness was Alvin Adams, the head of the Adams Express Company, a stagecoach firm that was transporting much of the gold being mined in the West. He testified:

> . . . At the time I visited the said grove Mr. Trask was engaged in taking the bark from one for the purpose of exhibiting it in the Atlantic States and Europe, and to the best of my knowledge and belief, the one now on exhibition at the Crystal Palace in the City of New York, is the same identical tree which I then saw, the bark of which I know to have been removed. Given under my hand and seal this 15th day of August, 1855.
>
> ALVIN ADAMS

Aided by such promotional gimmickry, the Mother of the Forest drew huge crowds all summer. Trask had let it be known at the outset that the tree would be on view only for a few months prior to being displayed in London, and from late August on his advertisements called attention to the fact that the exhibition would close on October 1. The proprietors of the Crystal Palace were sorry to see the tree go, for it was practically the only attraction left in their ill-starred hall; but despite their pleas, Trask ended his New York run on the announced date and shipped his giant tree across the Atlantic to London, where it would be displayed in another and grander Crystal Palace.

This was the original Crystal Palace, of which the New York hall was only a poor imitation. Prince Albert, the husband of Queen Victoria, had lent his support in 1848 to the idea of a "Great Exhibition" that would offer specimens of all that was notable in art, science, and nature—a combination of a museum and a World's Fair, in a single building. After much debate in Parliament, where the expensive project was bitterly opposed, Prince Albert had his way and the architect Joseph Paxton was placed in charge of constructing the building. Paxton had just designed what was then the largest greenhouse in the world, for the Duke of Devonshire, and his plan for the Crystal Palace was in effect an even bigger greenhouse—a structure of iron and glass, nearly a quarter of a mile long. Erected in London's Hyde Park, it opened on May 1, 1851, with such success that a group in New York was inspired to put up a smaller version of it there.

Though the exhibition at London's Crystal Palace was truly an array of wonders, meeting enthusiastic popular interest, Londoners complained over the presence of the vast building amid the pleasant greenery of Hyde Park. Yielding, Paxton began to take apart his masterpiece and move it piecemeal to Sydenham, south of London, where he reconstructed it in even grander form. When Trask arrived in London late in 1855, he found the intended exhibit hall midway in the process of transplantation, and there was no other building in or around London big enough to house his tree.

The greater part of the bark had to be put into storage. Trask did set up a section only 16 feet high for public exhibit in the spring of 1856, in the Philharmonic Rooms in Oxford Street, moving it after a few months to a larger hall in the Strand. It gave some idea of the diameter of the big tree, but not of its amazing height, and served merely to sharpen England's curiosity. The curious had to wait, though, until April 10, 1857, when the new Crystal Palace opened and the full 116-foot majesty of the Mother of the Forest could be seen at the north end of the building. The official catalogue of the exhibits offered this description, casually expanding the original tree still farther beyond its actual 321-foot height:

> We are now standing at the foot of what represents one of the largest known trees in the world. This tree grew, one of a group of such monsters, on the Sierra Nevada in California. When flourishing it rose to the astonishing height of nearly 400 feet. Several in the same district, which are now standing, are 300 feet in height. The bark of this tree has been arranged and fitted up as it grew, to give us some idea of its gigantic proportions by the view of the part. The wood is a particularly light cedar. Dr. Lindley [a British botanist]

Slab from a big tree on exhibit.

has named it *Wellingtonia gigantea*, and has fixed its age as 4,000 years.

Just how Dr. Lindley arrived at this estimate is hard to tell, since, as we know, the most reliable way of determining a tree's age is by counting its growth rings, and the Mother of the Forest had not been felled. Neither Dr. Lindley nor anyone else had any real idea of how many rings could be counted in her trunk. The stump of the nearby Hanford tree, despite its great width, had turned out to be only 1,300 years old by the growth-ring count.

The figure of 4,000 years for the Mother of the Forest became generally accepted, though, and resulted in such comments as that of the London *Times*, which said on April 11, 1857, that the Lindley estimate gave "an almost fabulous antiquity for a tree which was lately green and flourishing. According to this estimate it must have been growing when Nineveh was a mere collection of tents and ere the captive Jews began their labors on the Pyramids." The impact of discovering a living tree that old becomes all the greater when we realize that in 1857 most people believed that the world itself was only some fifty-nine centuries old. In the seventeenth century James Ussher, Archbishop of Armagh in Ireland, had announced that the creation of the world had taken place in 4004 B.C. He had arrived at this figure by adding up every bit of chronological information in the Bible, beginning with the age of Adam, the age of Adam's children, and the ages of *their* children, and so on down to the time of Christ. Although the Ussher theory had been under attack by scientists since the late eighteenth century, and would be exploded altogether by fossil discoveries later in the nineteenth century, it was still accepted by most laymen at the time of the Crystal Palace show. How awesome, then, to behold the remains of a tree that was more than two-thirds as old as the earth! The Mother of the Forest must have sprouted only a century or two after the Deluge of Noah's time—which, Archbishop Ussher said, took place in 2349 B.C.!

The British were thrilled by the tree, whose very immensity seemed so terribly American, so wonderfully appropriate to that land of oversized things. On the first day of the exhibition alone, 27,000 people packed the Crystal Palace at Sydenham, creating a perpetual jam of humanity before the Mother of the Forest. In the years that followed, the giant sequoia remained among the most popular exhibits in the hall, and so Trask left it on permanent display there, until it was destroyed in 1866 by fire.

VII
The Felling of the Trees

Thus the destruction of the giants began almost with their discovery. Within two years after the hunter Dowd brought word of the giant sequoias to Murphy's Camp, one of the big trees was cut down and another cruelly stripped of its bark. About the same time, the gold rush in California was setting in motion the first devastating wave of logging in the groves of coast redwoods.

Few voices were raised against the slaughter. The middle of the nineteenth century was not a time when many Americans worried about the conservation of natural resources; the continent seemed so huge that it was impossible to believe that anything might run out. Coal (and later, oil) was consumed with no thought of tomorrow; whole forests were leveled to make room for farms; the millions of bison in the prairie herds were hunted almost to the brink of extinction; the tasty passenger pigeon, once the most common bird in North America, was driven over that brink; and in the Far West, lumbermen tackled their mightiest challenge, the sequoias, with greedy delight. There were so many trees! Who would miss a few? Two million acres of redwoods! Unknown groves of giant sequoias awaiting discovery!

The redwoods were incredibly tempting to the loggers. Not only was the wood strong, durable, and attractive, but the great number of trees per acre promised fantastic profits. A redwood forest is probably the densest on earth, in terms of the quantity of commercial timber per acre. The huge trees stand in close array; as the geographer Henry Gannett wrote in 1899, "In a redwood forest the sun never shines—it is always twilight. You are, as it were, under the roof of a vast temple, a roof of foliage, supported by great tree columns."

In those dimly lit forests the timber merchants saw the bright glint of gold. They were accustomed to the forests of the east, where a yield of 5,000 board feet of timber per acre was considered excellent. In California's Mendocino County, though, the average stand of redwood across 173,000 acres was 44,000 board feet per acre—nine times that of the Southeastern states whose forests were producing most of the country's timber at the time. In Humboldt County, where there were nearly 100,000 acres of virgin redwood, the average stand could supply 84,000 board feet per acre—seventeen times the yield of the Eastern forests. Even the most heavily forested spruce and fir and pine country of Oregon and Washington could not compare with the redwood groves; the average there was only 28,000 feet per acre.

When the loggers went to work on the redwood stands, they found the actual yields even more astounding than the early estimates indicated. In the vicinity of Eureka, California, the heart of the redwood-logging industry of the late nineteenth century, a number of lumber companies averaged 75,000 to 100,000 feet of timber per acre for decades. One company cut 84,000 feet of redwood per acre for ten years in a tract that also yielded 20,000 feet per acre of fir and spruce. Another company averaged 150,000 feet per acre over several square miles for many years. One single acre of redwoods near Garberville, California, yielded an unbelievable 1,431,530 feet of lumber in the mill. There was enough lumber on this acre to have covered it with a solid block of wooden buildings ten stories high.

These statistics, impressive even to us, were celestial music to the owners of the lumber companies. But prosaic talk of feet per acre had a way of concealing the ugly fact that irreplaceable forest giants thousands of years old were toppling. One tree chopped down near Eureka in 1898 yielded more than 100,000 board feet of timber, even though the sawmill disdained to cut its branches and ignored any part of the tree disfigured by knots; those 100,000 feet of timber represented a majestic tree more than 300 feet tall and over 16 feet in diameter.

Logging these monsters in the nineteenth century was a project of heroic scope, if not exactly of heroic motive. When a team of loggers moved into a grove, the first step was to build a platform around the base of each tree to be felled, so that the lumberjacks would not have to cut at ground level where the trunk was thickest. Measurements were taken to see if the tree stood straight or leaned; the direction of its fall had to be calculated in advance, for if it fell the wrong way it might shatter into useless fragments. While a crew prepared a bed of small trees and branches to cushion the giant's descent, two men with axes would mount the platform and begin chopping, until they had cut halfway through the tree on one side. Then they used a twelve-foot crosscut saw to cut through from the other side. It was rough, exhausting work, but two skilled men, moving in expert coordination, could bring down a redwood twelve feet in diameter in three days. (In the twentieth century, the gasoline-powered chain saw replaced the old handsaws, and now any pygmy can chop down the mightiest of giants in an hour or two.)

Most of the logging was done in the winter rainy season, when the ground was soft and made a better cushion for a falling tree. Despite precautions, many trees broke into splinters as they fell, or dropped onto one of their fallen comrades and smashed it; but no matter, since nothing important had been wasted except the loggers' time—there were plenty of trees left!

Those trunks that had fallen properly were left on the ground until late spring, when the forest was drier. Then the loggers returned, and the first thing they did was to set forest fires, by way of simplifying their work. The fires

Logs weighing up to 20 tons apiece were chained together and hauled by cattle to the nearest river.

cleared away underbrush and removed most of the bark from the trunks, so that loggers could conveniently proceed to the task of cutting the trees into manageable logs. The grim effects produced by this casual time-saving device were described by one Californian about 1900:

> How often, in the hottest of the summer, have I not wished bad luck to the suffocating smoke that covers our beautiful scenery as with a black pall, day after day, hiding the face of Ben Lomond [a local mountain] with an unsightly veil, and increasing the temperature by at least ten degrees. If you ask, "Where is the fire?—it must be doing a great deal of damage," the aborigine of the mountains will answer with the utmost indifference, "Oh, no; they are only burning brush in the Big Basin." Sounds quite harmless, does it not?
>
> But the burning away of the underbrush means this: a certain section has been designated, or rather doomed, by the owner, to be cleared. . . . The torch is applied some fine dark night, and everything in that section—the birds in their nests, the merry little tree squirrel, the swift deer and the spotted fawn, the giant ferns and the rare orchids—everything is burned to death. The enormous trunks of the redwoods, green and full of sap, alone resist the fire-fiend; tops, branches, bark, are all burned to ashes, and madroños, oaks, firs, and young redwood trees are reduced to cinders and pitiful-looking black stumps.

When the fires had burned themselves out, the lumberjacks cut the trunks with handsaws into logs that were usually 16 feet long, although longer logs were sometimes cut to special order. For ease in handling, the big logs were split into halves and quarters; then came the job of getting these sections, still colossal, out of the forest. A number of logs, weighing up to 20 tons apiece, were chained together and hauled by teams of six to eight huge bulls or oxen down a "skid road" made of clay or small logs, kept slippery by frequent wetting-down. The cattle pulled the long strings of massive logs to the nearest river. Men known as "jackscrewers" dumped the logs into the river, swollen from spring floods, and floated them downstream to the sawmills. About 1880 the first logging railroads were built in redwood country, and gradually the need to float logs to the sawmills disappeared; the oxen now simply dragged the lumber to the railroad.

The toiling cattle themselves began to vanish from the logging scene after 1881, when a timber operator named John Dolbeer invented the "Dolbeer donkey," a powerful engine capable of transporting even the biggest logs. The "donkey" was anchored to stumps in the forest by a wire cable, so that when it went into action it would move a log toward itself and not itself toward the log. Another wire cable, attached to a drum on the engine, was carried through pulleys to the log to be moved, and was attached by hooks. Then the donkey operator opened his engine wide; the drum turned, reeling in the cable and whipping the log out of the woods. These donkeys were terribly destructive, for as they pulled some immense log forward, the log acted like a colossal bulldozer, plowing the soil and crushing all young trees in its path. A district that had been logged with donkey engines usually became a wasteland where only scrubby underbrush would grow; yet these machines remained in use until about 1935, when they were replaced by heavy-duty crawler tractors, which did less damage.

The slaughter of the redwoods went on enthusiastically for decades. The loggers did not try to leave young trees standing to become a timber harvest for future generations. Instead, starting near San Francisco and moving toward the untouched and seemingly infinite stands of redwood farther to the north, they cleared out every tree that could be logged, leaving huge areas completely bare so that they could be settled by homesteaders moving up from San Francisco. Serene redwood groves became vineyards, cow pastures, or sheep meadows.

The homesteaders were compelled to struggle mightily, though, against the unwillingness of the redwoods to stay dead. From roots, stumps, and burls, new trees sprouted on the cleared land. John Muir wrote, "All the brains, religion, and superstition of the neighborhood are brought into play to prevent a new growth. The sprouts from the roots and stumps are cut off again and again, with zealous concern as to the best time and method of making death sure. In the clearings of one of the largest mills on the coast we found thirty men at work, last summer, cutting off redwood shoots 'in the dark of the moon,' claiming that all the stumps and roots cleared at this auspicious time would send up no more shoots."

The desolation spread, for the hunger for redwood timber was insatiable. By 1899, 250,000,000 board feet of redwood were being cut each year, not counting the immense wastage involved in discarding trees that shattered in logging and branches that were too much bother to strip of bark and leaves. Within a few years, the annual cut had doubled. It remained at 500,000,000 feet a year until the 1930's, when the Great Depression caused it to dip somewhat, but by now it is well over a billion feet a year. The wood was put to a startling variety of uses. In his 1923 book, *The Trees of California,* Dr. W. L. Jepson wrote:

> The writer of these lines is a Californian. He was rocked by a pioneer mother in a cradle made of redwood. The house in which he lived was largely made of redwood. His clothing, the books of his juvenile library, the saddle for his rid-

ing pony were brought in railway cars chiefly made of redwood, running on rails laid on redwood ties, their course controlled by wires strung on redwood poles. He went to school in a redwood schoolhouse, sat at a desk made of redwood and wore shoes the leather of which was tanned in redwood vats. Everywhere he touched redwood. Boxes, bins, bats, barns, bridges, bungalows, were made of redwood. Posts, porches, piles, pails, pencils, pillars, paving-blocks, pipe lines . . . were made of redwood. . . .

During the years when some of the finest of the redwood trees were toppling, the giant sequoias of the Sierra Nevada were faring a little better. The biggest of them tended to grow in rough mountainous terrain, almost impossible to reach. If they could be reached, most of them were too big to be chopped down by nineteenth-century methods in any practical span of time. And those that could be chopped down were difficult to transport to any likely site for a sawmill. Today's loggers, with their high-powered chain saws, their tractors, and their steel cables for toppling partly sawed trees, would make short work of the giant sequoias, but happily the titans were beyond the reach of the lumber industry before mechanized logging came into being.

Plenty of damage was done before the big trees were protected, though. No more giants were skinned alive to be sent on exhibition after 1854, but a good many were felled for lumber. The logging got under way on a large scale about 1862, and reached its peak between 1880 and 1900, when the most accessible groves of giant sequoias were completely destroyed.

Much of this logging was a foolish waste. The giant sequoia's wood, unlike that of the redwood, does not really make very good lumber at all. It has only one outstanding characteristic: resistance to decay. (John Muir found one

Men called "jackscrewers" floated logs downstream to the sawmills.

fallen tree that had rested on the damp ground, he estimated, for perhaps a thousand years, but its wood "neither in color, strength, nor soundness could be distinguished from specimens cut from living trees.") But *gigantea's* wood is brittle and easily broken. Most of the logged trees shattered into small pieces when they fell. Those that came down intact were so big that the loggers dynamited them in order to split them into maneuverable logs, usually ruining most of the tree in the process. About the best way the wood could be put to use afterward was as vineyard stakes and shingles, hardly a fitting fate for these emperors of the forest.

Still, to a lumberman a tree is something to be chopped down, and thousands of giant sequoias were converted into stakes and shingles, and thousands more into useless waste.

(Sometimes the tree defeated the loggers. In General Grant Grove of Kings Canyon National Park stands the Sawed Tree, which was cut nearly through but would not fall. The tree lived, and by now has healed over the saw cut.)

Slowly the idea grew that there might be more profit, as well as more virtue, in preserving the big trees as tourist attractions than in cutting them down. That had been evident from the start at the Calaveras Grove, which had established itself in the 1850's as a necessary stop for sightseeing visitors to California. The stump of the first tree to fall there— the one Captain Hanford had cut down for exhibition—became a popular gathering place. A pavilion was erected on it, in which shows were sometimes produced, and later a bowling alley was laid out on the stump. Another tree was named "the Horseback Ride"; it was a fallen tree that had been hollowed by fire, leaving a tunnel through which a man on horseback could pass. In 1863, though, this tree split and caved in.

Visitors delighted in giving names to outstanding trees. For a while these names could be carved on marble slabs sold by one enterprising concessionaire, and attached to the trees. Some of the names tended toward the poetic, such as "Pride of the Forest," "Fallen Hercules," and "The Three Graces." Others were named for the home states of the tourists, or for great Americans: Washington, Daniel Webster, Henry Clay, Longfellow. Two trees were named Ada and Mary, "for the first two ladies who ever came here in a buggy." As the trees of Calaveras Grove acquired names and, so to speak, personalities, the thought that they might someday be cut down began to seem horrifying to more and more Americans. Yet lumbermen continued to eye the Calaveras trees greedily, bringing from John Muir the sarcastic remark, "No doubt these trees would make good lumber after

101

passing through a sawmill, as George Washington after passing through the hands of a French cook would have made good food." Thanks to the outcries of such men as Muir, most of the Calaveras trees were spared, although the grove itself did not pass from private ownership until 1931, when it became Calaveras Big Trees State Park.

In the 1860's a second grove of giant sequoias, more amazing even than the Calaveras Grove, began to overshadow Calaveras as a center for tourism. This was the Mariposa Grove in the future Yosemite National Park. The Yosemite Valley had been glimpsed by a few explorers in the 1830's and 1840's, but it was officially discovered in 1851, when Major James D. Savage and his battalion pursued a band of Indian raiders into the steep granite gorge. A young army doctor, Lafayette Bunnell, accompanied Savage and his men and gave names to many of the valley's most stunning features, as well as naming the valley itself. He called it Yosemite after the name of the Indian tribe that occupied it, a name supposedly meaning "grizzly bear" in their language. By 1855, the first sightseers were touring the valley, and not long afterward the Mariposa sequoias were discovered—or rediscovered, since they may have been seen by the Walker expedition in 1833.

The big trees of Yosemite were quickly removed from the danger of logging. The entire valley belonged, like most of the land west of the Mississippi, to the United States Government, and in 1864 Congress passed and President Lincoln signed a law setting the valley and the giant sequoias aside "for public use, resort and recreation . . . for all time." There was not yet any national park system, and so the Government turned this 40-square-mile tract over to the State of California to be administered as a state park.

A few years later, there came to Yosemite the man whose

name is most closely associated with the saving of the sequoias: John Muir. Born in Scotland in 1838, Muir was unable to settle down to any career, but spent his life wandering "like a leaf in every eddy," as he said, following "a planless route." Through swamps and valleys, up mountains, across moors and plains, he roamed tirelessly, observing trees, plants, butterflies, rocks, anything that engaged his boundless curiosity. He loved the wilderness and feared neither hunger nor danger; he carried no gun, and went without food much of the time. To prepare for an expedition, he declared, all he had to do was to "throw some tea and bread in an old sack and jump over the back fence."

He was also an inventor, and even before his wanderings had brought him to the United States he had produced a number of ingenious devices. Among them were an improved sawmill—an ironical invention for a man who was to spend most of his life fighting the timber barons—and an unusually sensitive thermometer. An extraordinary Muir-designed clock struck the hours, told the date, lit the fire in his stove and the oil in his lamp, and, by means of levers and gears, tilted his bed up to awaken him at the scheduled time every morning.

After a mill accident cost him the sight of one eye in 1867, Muir decided to devote the rest of his life to exploring his beloved wilderness world. "As long as I live," he wrote, "I'll hear waterfalls and birds and winds sing, I'll interpret the rocks, learn the language of flood, storm, and the avalanche. I'll acquaint myself with the glaciers and wild gardens, and get as near the heart of the world as I can." He began by walking a thousand miles from Indiana to the Gulf of Mexico; and in 1868 he reached Yosemite, which he called "the most holy mansion of the mountains." Here he stared in awe and wonder at the giant sequoias; and then he moved on through the Sierra Nevada to the Pacific Northwest, and into remote Alaska.

The big trees fascinated him more, perhaps, than anything else he had seen, and he returned to them again and again. Those of Yosemite were in no danger, but Muir feared that loggers would beat the park builders to the other groves. On each of his visits he listened anxiously for the sound of saws and axes, and wondered how much time remained before the greatest of the trees fell to the lumbermen.

One of Muir's most rewarding trips through the Sierra Nevada giant sequoia country was one that he began in August 1875. Usually he went alone and on foot, carrying as little as possible, but on this journey he had a companion —an agile little brown mule to carry provisions and blankets, since Muir planned this to be a long jaunt. He made his first camp in Yosemite's Mariposa Grove, already much visited, and spent almost a week there, hoping to find more giant sequoias adjoining those already discovered.

He saw none, and set out toward the southeast, into a forest that had not yet been explored. No giant sequoias came into view until Muir climbed a lofty cliff and looked into the valley of the Fresno River. Here, Muir wrote, "innumerable spires of the noble yellow pine were displayed rising one above another on the braided slopes, and yet nobler sugar pines with superb arms outstretched in the rich autumn light, while away toward the southwest, on the verge of the glowing horizon, I discovered the majestic domelike crowns of Big Trees towering high over all, singly and in close grove congregations."

Running back to his camp, Muir packed his mule and headed down into the heart of this grove. He settled beside a brook, made a cup of tea, and went forth to explore these giants. "One of the first special things that caught my

John Muir, who sought help from Congress to save the giant sequoias from destruction.

attention," he wrote, "was an extensive landslip. The ground on the side of a stream had given way to a depth of about fifty feet, and with all its trees had been launched into the bottom of the stream ravine. Most of the trees—pines, firs, incense cedar, and Sequoia—were still standing erect and uninjured, as if unconscious that anything out of the common had happened." Muir was cheered to see a great many sequoia seedlings and saplings growing on the freshly turned soil along the landslide's front face: "These young trees were already eight or ten feet high, and were shooting up vigorously, as if sure of eternal life. . . . Farther down the ravine I counted five hundred and thirty-six promising young Sequoia on a bed of rough bouldery soil not exceeding two acres in extent."

While in this grove Muir discovered a hermit—"an old, weary-eyed, unspeculative, gray-haired man"—living in a log cabin. He was John A. Nelder, a forty-niner who had failed to strike it rich, and who had been living alone among the forest giants to wait out his last days. Muir tells how Nelder "tenderly stroked the little snow-bent sapling Sequoias, hoping they might yet grow straight to the sky and rule the grove. One of the greatest of his trees stands a little way back of his cabin, and he proudly led me to it, bidding me admire its colossal proportions and measure it, to see if in all the forest there could be another so grand. It proved to be only twenty-six feet in diameter, and he seemed distressed to learn that the Mariposa Grizzly Giant was larger. I tried to comfort him by observing that his was the taller, finer formed, and perhaps the more favorably situated." (The Grizzly Giant is the fifth largest known giant sequoia, in terms of bulk. Though only 209 feet tall, it has a diameter of nearly 28 feet, is 96.5 feet in circumference, and contains 30,300 cubic feet of wood.)

The grove where the hermit dwelt covered about four square miles, making it one of the biggest groupings of giant sequoias ever discovered. "One of the most interesting features of this grove," said Muir, "is the apparent ease and strength and comfortable independence in which the trees occupy their place in the general forest. Seedlings, saplings, young and middle-aged trees, are grouped promisingly around the old patriarchs, betraying no sign of approach to extinction. On the contrary, all seem to be saying, 'Everything is to our mind, and we mean to live forever.'" But the promise of these young trees was not destined to be fulfilled. "Sad to tell," Muir added, "a lumber company was building a large mill and flume near by, assuring widespread destruction." Logging operations began only a few years after Muir's 1875 visit, and many of the biggest trees were cut down. Today the Nelder Grove, as it is called, is part of Sierra National Forest, but only some 200 acres of giant sequoias remain—less than a third of a square mile.

Leaving the hermit, Muir and his mule moved on, "day after day, from grove to grove, canyon to canyon," traveling "a long wavering way; terribly rough in some places for Brownie, but cheery for me, for Sequoias were seldom out of sight." In the valley of the Kaweah, Muir came one day at sundown to a sequoia grove so mighty that he named it the Giant Forest. "It extends," he wrote, "a magnificent growth of giants, grouped in pure temple groves, ranged in colonnades along the sides of meadows, or scattered among the other trees, from the granite headlands overlooking the hot foothills and plains of the San Joaquin back to within a few miles of the old glacier fountains, at an elevation of five thousand to eight thousand four hundred feet above the sea."

He walked through the groves until night had fallen; then he made his simple supper, "and lay on my back, looking

107

up to the stars through pillared arches. . . ." By moonlight, the trees "seemed still more marvelously massive and tall than by day, heaving their colossal heads into the depths of the sky among the stars, some of which seemed to be sparkling on their branches like flowers." At dawn Muir was up and exploring his beloved trees, and all through the long, mellow autumn day he wandered among them, watching the changing colors from hour to hour. Suddenly the spell was broken: a man on horseback appeared at the far end of the grove. Muir stepped out where he could be seen, and shouted to draw the other man's attention.

The man on horseback was a rancher named Hale Tharp, who had been grazing his livestock in the Kaweah Valley for many years. Tharp had become friendly with the Yokuts Indians of the valley, who led him one day in 1858 into a place of unbelievable trees—one of the largest groves of giant sequoias in existence. Tharp returned in 1860, and made a summer home for himself, 58 feet long and 8 feet high, in a single fallen sequoia that had been hollowed out by fire. Adding a door, window, chimney, and entrance foyer, Tharp occupied his tree house every summer while his herds were in the valley.

For seventeen years—until this meeting with Muir in the late summer of 1875—Tharp had been the only white man to know of the Giant Forest. Now he was so surprised at seeing a stranger that he could not speak, and it was Muir who hailed him, saying he was glad to meet a fellow mountaineer in such a lonely place.

"What are you doing?" Tharp demanded. "How did you get here?"

Muir explained that he had come "across the canyons from Yosemite, and was only looking at the trees."

"Oh, then I know," Tharp replied, greatly to the wanderer's amazement. "You must be John Muir."

Tharp was herding a band of horses up from the lowlands to graze in the forest meadows. Since Muir was nearly out of food, he asked the rancher if he could spare a little flour. "Oh, yes, of course, you can have anything I've got," Tharp said. "Just take my track, and it will lead you to my camp in a big hollow log on the side of a meadow two or three miles from here. I must ride after some strayed horses, but I'll be back before night; in the meantime make yourself at home." He galloped off to the north.

Muir's account relates how he saddled Brownie and arrived, by midafternoon, at Tharp's cabin—a "noble den in a fallen Sequoia hollowed by fire,—a spacious log house of one log, carbon-lined, centuries old, yet sweet and fresh, weatherproof, earthquake-proof, likely to outlast the most durable stone castle, and commanding views of garden and grove grander far than the richest king ever enjoyed." Soon Tharp came in, and the two mountaineers ate and talked a long while about the great trees.

There were hundreds of giants here, including the biggest big tree of all, the one that later would be called the General Sherman Tree, and also the 291-footer that would be the McKinley Tree, the 250-foot President Tree, and the vast Lincoln Tree, 259 feet high and 31 feet in diameter at the base. Here, too, Muir witnessed the spectacular forest fire that called forth such lyrical prose from him. Then he moved on to the south, into the valley of the Tule River, where other giant sequoia groves awaited him; and at last he realized he had come to the end of the empire of the giants, which he had traced from north to south for its full 250 miles.

It had been a journey of wonders and marvels, but at journey's end Muir's exhilaration was mingled with forebodings and fears. The trees he had seen—would they survive into the twentieth century? Or would his path of discovery be followed by saw-wielding lumberjacks? Even while he had dined in Hale Tharp's sequoia-log cabin, the slayers of the trees had been working in Converse Basin, not many miles away. Groves rivaling the Giant Forest itself had existed there, but now the sequoias were falling by the hundreds. (The logging would continue year after year until, by 1900, some 6,000 acres of giant sequoias, the largest single sequoia forest, would be almost completely cut over. Today the Converse Basin is a somber graveyard of colossal stumps, over which the third largest of all the giant sequoias, which somehow survived the carnage, presides—the Boole Tree, 112 feet in circumference and 269 feet high.)

The Yosemite big trees were safe, Muir knew; but all the others were at the mercy of man. Could anything be done to protect them? "Any fool can destroy trees," he wrote. "They cannot run away; and if they could they would still be destroyed—chased and hunted down as long as fun or a dollar could be got out of their bark hides, branching horns, or magnificent bole backbones. . . . God has cared for these trees [sequoias], saved them from drought, disease, avalanches, and a thousand straining, leveling tempests and floods; but he cannot save them from fools—only Uncle Sam can do that." And to Uncle Sam John Muir took his campaign to save the giant sequoias while there still was time.

VIII
Saving the Trees

In the early years of the twentieth century President Theodore Roosevelt declared: "I feel most emphatically that we should not turn into shingles a tree which was old when the first Egyptian conquerors penetrated to the valley of the Euphrates, which it has taken so many thousands of years to build up, and which can be put to better use. That, you may say, is not looking at the matter from the practical standpoint. There is nothing more practical in the end than the preservation of beauty, than the preservation of anything that appeals to the higher emotions in mankind."

At the time he spoke those words, much of the battle to save the giant sequoias had been won—although the last skirmishes of that battle continued into our own day. Men like John Muir, publisher George W. Stewart of Visalia, California, and Gustavus Eisen of the California Academy of Science had persuaded an often reluctant Congress to set apart the most important giant sequoia groves as national treasures.

The first step in that direction had been the act of 1864 that preserved the Mariposa Grove of Yosemite Valley as a

park under the administration of the State of California. Then, on March 1, 1872, Congress created Yellowstone National Park. There are no sequoias in Yellowstone, except for petrified ones millions of years old; but the establishment of this park was important because it introduced the concept of national parks under national ownership. Individual states did not always treat their natural wonders well; with a system of national parks, it was possible to set up standards under which the scenic resources of the country would be protected on behalf of the entire nation.

It was a long time before that system of national parks came into being, though. For nearly twenty years Yellowstone was our only national park. During that time Muir and others argued for the creation of other parks in the West, before the logging and mining interests had a chance to ruin the beauty of that unspoiled region. Since most of the land belonged to the Government anyway, it would be an easy matter to set up such parks. But many Congressmen were more interested in seeing their friends in the business world grow wealthy than they were in founding parks in the West; hardly anybody, they said, would bother to make the dangerous trip out there, through Indian-infested country, and why should the country give up the profits that could be made from exploiting the land? Under the Homestead Act of 1862, any bona fide settler could buy up to 160 acres of government land at $1.25 an acre, and that, said the Congressmen, was what the West was for—to be settled, to be conquered. Of course, the big timber operators were quietly and dishonestly putting together large tracts of redwood and giant sequoia land by hiring phony homesteaders to buy the land in 160-acre units from the Government, but nearly

"Any fool can destroy trees," said John Muir. "They cannot run away."

everyone winked at that; a little bribery took care of the objectors.

In 1881, as a result of public appeals, bills were introduced in Congress that would have set aside, either as a national park or as a forest preserve, the whole eastern slope of the Sierra Nevada from Yosemite south to the Kern River. This would have placed nearly all of the giant sequoia area under government control. But the territory was too large, the bills too sweeping, and they failed to pass.

Muir would not give up. His prodding brought success in 1890 on three fronts. On September 25, 1890, Sequoia National Park was created—the second of our national parks. It extended across the whole basin of the Kaweah River, and removed much of the Giant Forest from the perils of logging. A week later, Congress set up a third national park nearby: General Grant National Park (later included in Kings Canyon National Park), which contained the Grant Grove of giant sequoias, including the General Grant Tree, the General Lee Tree, the California Tree, and many others of great size. And on October 1, 1890, the law establishing national park number four—Yosemite National Park—was passed. This park covered an area of some 1,200 square miles completely surrounding the old 40-square-mile state park in the Yosemite Valley itself, and brought under protection the Merced and Tuolumne groves of giant sequoias. (The curious arrangement of having a state park within a national park lasted until 1906, when California returned the Yosemite Valley to the Federal Government and it was merged into Yosemite National Park.)

These dramatic developments eliminated the danger that all but a token few of the big trees might be wiped out by logging. Nevertheless, John Muir felt that much remained to be done. "Through man's agency destruction is making rapid progress," he declared, "while in the work of protection only a beginning has been made." Writing in 1900, he pointed out that "perhaps more than half of all the Big Trees have been sold, and are now in the hands of speculators and mill-men. Even the beautiful little Calaveras Grove of ninety trees, and so historically interesting from its being the first discovered, is now owned, together with the much larger South or Stanislaus Grove, by a lumber company." Nor were the two national parks, General Grant and Sequoia, truly sanctuaries for the big trees. The parks were pock-marked with private land holdings whose owners were free to cut down some of the finest sequoia stands. Muir called upon the Government to purchase these privately held areas, which he said should never have been sold to individuals in the first place. The cost would not be high, he argued, since the giant sequoia was not really a valuable lumber tree, despite the blind insistence of lumbermen on cutting it down.

Slowly the Government acted to do Muir's bidding. In 1893 the Sequoia Forest Preserve, later known as Sequoia National Forest, was set up. Unlike a national park, where no interference with nature is allowed, some logging is permitted in a national forest. But it was understood that none of the numerous giant sequoias in this preserve would be touched.

Sequoia National Forest contains about twenty sequoia groves, some of them quite small and practically impossible to reach. Others, like Mountain Home Forest, are among the most important groves of all. Mountain Home contains the Sawed Off Tree, which was cut completely through by loggers but refused to fall, and the Hercules Tree, which still lives despite the cutting of a large room in its heart many years ago.

Little was done to save other giant sequoias over the next

twenty years, though public-spirited citizens did raise funds to purchase a few small groves from lumber companies and turn them into parks. And the lumber companies did take a more public-spirited attitude after 1900, refraining from cutting the biggest of the trees they owned.

During World War I, the price of lumber rose along with the prices of all other commodities, and there was some talk of logging the privately owned trees in the Giant Forest of Sequoia National Park. To prevent this, the Department of the Interior asked Congress to vote $50,000 for the purchase of a 667-acre holding within the national park. By the time Congress agreed to provide the money, though, the price of the land had risen to $70,000. The owners of the land were persuaded to give the Department of the Interior some time to raise the extra $20,000; but by now Christmas was approaching, the Congressmen were rushing to adjourn, and there was no hope of getting the busy lawmakers to think about giant sequoias once more. In the emergency, the National Geographic Society stepped in with a contribution of $20,000, and the trees were purchased and added to Sequoia National Park.

In 1920 the National Geographic provided $21,330 more, enough to cover the purchase of three additional privately owned tracts totaling 609 acres within the park's boundaries. This time the money did not come out of the Geographic's own funds, but was contributed by three members of the Society: Stephen T. Mather, the head of the National Park Service, D. E. Skinner of Seattle, and Louis Titus of Washington, D.C. Only 640 acres of private land now remained in Sequoia National Park, and this land was purchased in 1921 for $55,000, with funds from the Society, individuals,

Sequoia National Park

and Tulare County, California, where Sequoia National Park is located.

In 1926, the Federal Government doubled the size of Sequoia National Park, bringing it to its present 604 square miles. Five years later, the famous little Calaveras Grove, where all the excitement over big trees had started, became Calaveras Big Trees State Park. In 1938, President Franklin D. Roosevelt authorized the purchase of the splendid though misleadingly named Redwood Canyon Forest, which contains 2,500 acres of giant sequoias but no coast redwoods. Redwood Canyon adjoined General Grant National Park, and in 1940 the Government combined them into the new 710-square-mile Kings Canyon National Park, which lies just north of Sequoia National Park.

By that time about 92 percent of the larger specimens of giant sequoia had come under public control—mostly in the three national parks and in Sequoia and Sierra Nevada Forests, but a small percentage of trees were also on Indian reservations and in state and county parks. Of the trees that remained in private ownership, only one, the Stanislaus or South Calaveras Grove, was a major stand threatened by destruction. Located five miles from the Calaveras Grove this 1,000-acre grove contained 947 giant sequoias, half of them 10 feet or more in diameter. Among them is one of the largest trees of all, the Agassiz Tree, which is 30 feet in diameter and 250 feet tall. This grove was owned by the Pickering Lumber Corporation, which was making no immediate move to cut down the big trees; but negotiations for purchase of the grove dragged on for many years, seemingly on the point of failure several times, until at last the late John D. Rockefeller, Jr., bought the grove and presented it to the State of California.

Today the giant sequoias are beyond the reach of the destroyers. The old photographs showing gangs of lumberjacks struggling to cut down a single big tree will never be matched by modern counterparts, nor can a prophet arise to denounce the transformation of these noble trees into shingles and stakes. Yet some scientists are beginning to wonder if by saving the giant sequoias man has not also—strange as it may seem—exposed them to new dangers.

One such danger is that of root compaction. Every summer millions of visitors enter Yosemite National Park; traffic in Kings Canyon and Sequoia national parks, though not nearly so heavy, is also considerable. Almost all of these park visitors pay a call on the famous sequoias—General Sherman, General Grant, the Wawona Tree, the Grizzly Giant, and so on. They have trampled to death all the shrubbery around these trees, and have packed down the soil over the shallow root system of the giants; in some cases the soil has been compressed to a point several feet below its level of a generation ago. Some botanists feel that this wear and tear may be injuring the sequoias—that the admirers of the trees are doing them irreparable harm as they walk about in the groves.

The root-compaction problem is actually a fairly minor one. The National Park Service has erected fences around the most popular of the trees; and not all scientists agree that the packing down of the soil presents any real danger to begin with. Furthermore, most of the giant sequoias are located in remote groves unlikely to be visited by huge throngs.

A much more serious danger to the giant sequoias is the success of fire-prevention campaigns in the publicly owned forests.

This may seem upside down; how can *successful* fire prevention harm the trees? Shouldn't every effort be made to keep fire from sweeping through the sequoia groves?

Not at all, apparently. Fires pose no real threat to the giants, whose scarred trunks testify to their ability to withstand the fiercest blazes. On the contrary, it appears that periodic forest fires are necessary for the reproduction of the big trees!

The tiny seed of the giant sequoia can sprout only under very special conditions. It must be able to put its small root down into soil that is moist and rich in minerals; and since the seed is so extraordinarily little, it carries just a minute quantity of stored food to feed the plant while it is seeking to take root. If the forest floor is covered with a thick, dry layer of dead sequoia needles, the seedling will die before its emerging seed root can penetrate deeply enough into the soil to reach a nutritious level.

Therefore most giant sequoia seeds perish. Those that sprout are the few that land in an area where the litter of fallen leaves has been cleared away and the underlying mineral-laden soil is exposed. Young sequoias spring up where flooding streams have carried away the litter, where avalanches have scraped the soil bare, where falling sequoias have skidded, or where man has disturbed the ground by building roads or trails. The best places of all for the seeding of sequoias are those where fire has burned away the accumulated covering of forest debris.

Once a baby giant sequoia has managed to sprout, it needs a great deal of sunlight and soil moisture in order to survive. It does not have to worry about competition from the huge full-grown sequoias, since ordinarily they do not grow in close ranks, and the sparse foliage of a mature giant sequoia admits a good deal of sunlight to the forest floor. But other trees, such as white fir, incense cedar, or black oak, may form dense canopies that cut off the sun. Forest fires kill these lesser trees, leaving only the great giant se-

quoias standing, few and far between. In the openings between these trees there is ample sunlight for the young
sequoia saplings.

But what if there are no forest fires?

Since the giant sequoia groves passed into government
control, forest rangers have taken steps to prevent fires and
to extinguish quickly those that are started by lightning or
careless men. The last major fire in Yosemite's Mariposa
Grove occurred in 1862, two years before the grove was
given the status of a park. A smaller fire touched the edge
of the grove in 1889; there have been none of any importance since. But a study of the scarred growth rings of Mariposa sequoias shows that from 1760 to 1862 the grove had
endured a large fire on an average of once every seven or
eight years. During that time new sequoias were able to take
root and establish themselves in the intervals between fires,
as is shown by the presence of numerous trees 100 to 200
years old. However, in the last century, the absence of fires
has allowed a dense stand of white fir to spring up in the
grove. And the fir trees are preventing the growth of new
sequoias.

Since 1934, when park rangers began making serious
studies of the situation, only about thirty sequoias have
sprouted in the Mariposa Grove. They all have arisen in
areas disturbed by man, and most of them are packed so
closely together that just a few will survive to become giants.
A survey of thirty-one groves in Sequoia and Kings Canyon
national parks showed the same situation: seedlings and
saplings are rare. Now that there are no fires in the groves,
the ground is covered with deep layers of debris, so that
few sequoia seeds can sprout; and the trees that do sprout
are quickly killed by the deep shade cast by the new stands
of white fir.

The existing giant sequoias, of course, will live on for hundreds or thousands of years. But someday they will die, and where will their replacements come from, if no new sequoias are sprouting? Are we killing this mighty species by our efforts to protect it?

The lack of fires is also slowing the growth of the mature trees. In the past, when a fire cleared the forest of its lesser trees, the giants suddenly found themselves without competition for soil moisture, and began to grow at a rate two to four times as fast as usual. This can be seen by an examination of the growth rings of the trees: core samplings of the outer rings show a significant jump in growth rate corresponding to the period just after a major forest fire, with the rate slowing as new trees emerged in the seasons following the fire.

The solution to the problem appears to lie in "prescribed fires"—that is, fires deliberately set by park rangers to provide the big trees with the environment they need. Such fires, kindled under close control and at seasons best suited to the work, can burn off the underbrush in limited areas without threatening the safety of the whole region.

A philosophical difficulty is involved in setting prescribed fires. The act of Congress that set up the National Park Service in 1916 prohibits the park rangers from doing anything that would interfere with maintaining the park areas in their natural condition. The only exceptions to this are made for the sake of the public, for whom the parks are intended. Thus roads and hotels are built in the parks; dangerous animals are removed from regions where the public is likely to go; and fires are prevented. Is the deliberate setting of fires a violation of the law that the national parks must be left untouched as much as possible?

The National Park Service argues that since preventing

fires has disturbed the natural life of the giant sequoia groves, lighting prescribed fires would simply be a method of restoring the desired natural conditions. Under this line of reasoning, prescribed fires have come into use in Everglades National Park, Florida, where overzealous fire prevention was threatening to replace the plants of the pine forests and prairie marshes with different species. In 1965 experimental burning began in a secluded part of Kings Canyon National Park, so that rangers could determine the most effective way of insuring that new generations of giant sequoias will continue to appear, for the delight and amazement of those who may inhabit this continent five or ten thousand years hence.

By 1900 it was possible to say that the giant sequoia of the Sierra Nevada had been saved as a species. Most of the best trees were under protection and few of the others were threatened, because timber operators had come to see that the poor quality of the wood made it not worth trouble to log them. The situation was altogether different for the giant sequoia's lofty cousin, the redwood of the Pacific Coast. As the new century opened, not a single redwood tree could be considered safe from destruction. It was quite within possibility that the lumbermen would chop down every last one. "As timber," John Muir said angrily, "the redwood is too good to live."

The work of saving at least some of the finest old trees began in May 1900, with the founding of the Sempervirens Club of California. This organization had as its goal the establishment of a public park in redwood country; as a result of its campaign, the California legislature voted $250,000 for the purchase of 3,800 acres of redwoods in Big Basin, near Santa Cruz. Today that has become the

11,000-acre Big Basin Redwoods State Park, among the southernmost of the important redwood parks.

In 1907, Congressman William Kent bought 295 acres of redwoods in a canyon at the base of Mount Tamalpais, a short distance from San Francisco. A water company had wanted to flood the canyon for a reservoir; but the redwoods were saved by Kent who, in 1908, gave the land to the United States in honor of his friend John Muir. With a later gift Kent expanded the park to 510 acres, creating the present Muir Woods National Monument. This beautiful little grove of redwood giants receives more visitors than any other, because it is so close to San Francisco; nowhere else do redwoods grow within an hour's drive of a major city.

As World War I approached, the Muir Woods and Big Basin redwoods were the only ones in public hands, except for three very small tracts. The demand for redwood timber was growing from year to year. As Dr. W. L. Jepson wrote in 1923, "One of the most emphatic tributes to the economic value of redwood is that new uses are constantly being discovered for it. We ship our choicest grapes to distant lands packed in redwood sawdust. We replace steel water-conduits with redwood. We supply redwood doors to the Central American market because the white ant [the termite] does not eat redwood." New methods of logging were making it easier than ever to cut the titans down. At the rate the timber operators were chewing at the redwood forests, it began to seem as though the trees could not last another fifty years.

Of course, the lumbermen did not plan to wipe out the redwoods altogether. There were a few unscrupulous "cut out and get out" loggers who would sweep through a forest, taking every worthwhile tree and leaving behind such devastation that nothing but scrub could grow there afterwards; but the large lumber companies had no intention of logging themselves out of business within one or two generations. Good business sense required them to encourage the growth of young redwood trees, so that there would be future supplies of the valuable timber.

Unfortunately, good business sense also told the lumbermen to concentrate on cutting the largest and stateliest of the trees first. Obviously, the biggest redwoods contain the most timber; it was not much more effort to cut a 300-foot tree than a 150-foot tree, and the yield was a good deal more than twice as great. But there was another reason for going after the giants. A mature redwood—one that is a thousand years or more of age—grows very slowly, and keeps younger and shorter trees from getting sunlight and moisture. By getting one such giant out of the way, a dozen younger trees can be made to grow more swiftly. To a lumberman, the rate of growth of his uncut trees is all-important. A "static" forest is not nearly as desirable as one in which the trees yet to be cut are gaining in size and width from season to season.

So the colossi were toppling. Each year the logging roads pressed deeper into what had been virgin stands of redwood, and inaccessible groves of tall trees came within reach of the ax and the saw. During World War I the State of California decided to rebuild the highway that ran from San Francisco to the Oregon border through the most magnificent of redwood stands, and this seemed to be the death warrant for the great trees of northern California. Once a modern highway ran through Humboldt and Del Norte counties, the loggers would close in on the redwoods.

In the summer of 1917 three men interested in the conservation of nature went on a trip through Humboldt County's redwood country. None of them were Californians. Henry Fairfield Osborn of Connecticut was the president of the American Museum of Natural History; John C. Merriam of Iowa was professor of paleontology at the University of California; Madison Grant of New York was president of the New York Zoological Society. What they saw in Humboldt County dismayed them. Merriam wrote: "There are parts of the northwestern highways where for miles the road is narrowed and blocked with piled grape stakes and shingles, and on either hand the ground is covered with a jumble of treetops, branches, slabs and bark."

Yet it was not too late to save many superb groves. He went on: "Also there are stretches where the roadway leads from open sunshine and distant views of green, wooded mountain slopes into the giant forest and on through colonnades of trees where air is cool and fragrant and long beams of sunlight slant down through the green of redwood foliage." When they returned from their journey, the three men set up the Save-the-Redwoods League, which was formally organized in San Francisco in July 1919, under Merriam's direction. It proposed these aims:

1. To purchase redwood groves by private subscription and by county bond issues.
2. To secure a State bond issue to buy the finest redwood groves along State highways.
3. To establish, through Federal aid, a National Redwood Park.
4. To obtain, through State and county aid, the protection of timber along the scenic highways now in course of construction throughout California.
5. To encourage the State to purchase cut-over redwood areas for reforestation by natural means or by replanting where repeated fires have made sprout reproduction impossible.

Wealthy men contributed large sums to the League, but its leaders also appealed to the general public for two-dollar donations. These came in by the thousands, not just from

California but from all over the country. Magazine articles by League officers called attention to the danger facing the redwoods. Madison Grant, writing in a 1920 issue of the *National Geographic Magazine*, declared, "It is scarcely necessary to dwell on the need to put an end to the destruction of the oldest and tallest trees on earth. The cutting of a Sequoia for grape stakes or railroad ties (and an eighteen-foot tree along the new State highway was cut a few months ago for that purpose) is like breaking up one's grandfather's clock for kindling to save the trouble of splitting logs at the woodpile, or lighting one's pipe with a Greek manuscript to save the trouble of reaching for the matches."

He warned that "it will cost money to preserve the redwoods—many millions of dollars; but California has no choice. Either the amount needed to save the groves must be supplied today or else a far greater sum will be required ten years hence to purchase a butchered and isolated tenth part of the forests."

The Save-the-Redwoods League did not, however, want to save *every* redwood: "Of course, lumbering must go on," Grant wrote. "But most of the purposes for which redwood is now being used can be served from second-growth timber, and there are vast areas of denuded, devastated, and lumbered-over lands which can be made in a few years to supply all the timber needed." Young redwoods grow swiftly, he pointed out; let scientifically managed tree farms be set up to grow redwoods purely for lumbering, and halt the cutting of the giants that could not be replaced for two thousand years.

Now, he said, was the moment to save the best groves—before they fell, and before the price of the trees went beyond the reach of conservationists. "The fundamental tragedy of the whole redwood situation," Grant continued, "lies in the fact that the great trees are nearly all in the hands of private owners, who cannot reasonably be expected to sacrifice their holdings for public benefit. The State and nation, having given away these lands in the past, must now buy back at least a large portion of them."

In the summer of 1919, former Congressman William Kent and Stephen Mather of the National Park Service each gave $30,000 to the League for the purchase of Humboldt County land where some lumbering had already begun. At the last possible moment they saved the trees, before any great damage had been done, and the nucleus of California's future group of redwood parks took form.

The most ambitious goal of the Save-the-Redwoods League was to bring about the creation of a Redwood National Park in northern California, so that Federal protection would be given to *sempervirens* as it had already been given in three national parks to *gigantea*. But the Federal Government, under Presidents Harding, Coolidge, and Hoover, was more interested in reducing its expenses than in buying redwood land, and the League had to turn to the State of California for financial aid. The state was at work on the northern half of Highway 101, which was to pass right through the redwood forests; the League wished first to see to it that the fewest possible trees would be removed to make way for the road, and then that state parks would be established along the road so that the trees would be spared from logging.

In 1921 the League asked the state for a $300,000 appropriation to buy redwood lands for these parks. Under pressure from many conservation-minded Californians, the legislature passed the bill; but then Governor William D. Stephens hesitated to sign it. California was short of cash, the governor explained; it would be wiser, perhaps to spend that money on improving the schools. A delegation of conservationists led by William Kent visited Governor Stephens. "Hell, Bill," Kent said, "shut the schools down. The kids would enjoy it, and it would only take them a year or two to make the work up. If these trees all go, it will take two thousand years to make *them* up." The governor got the point and signed the bill.

In 1928 came another important victory: the state voted a $6,000,000 bond issue for the purchase of redwood lands. Interestingly, this measure was supported not only by the Save-the-Redwoods League but by two trade groups of lumbermen: the California Redwood Association and the National Lumber Manufacturers Association. In the new atmosphere of conservationism, even the timber operators were eager to see some of the finest redwoods preserved. So long as the League made it clear that they did not want *all* redwood logging halted, the owners of the best groves were willing to leave the grandest trees untouched while money was raised for their purchase.

This is not to say that the lumbermen did not ask high prices for their trees, or fail to increase the prices from time to time when they saw a chance for greater profit. And there always were some who made a point of cutting over their land as soon as they learned the League might be interested in it. Generally, though, the lumber companies behaved honorably during the years when California was assembling its network of redwood parks.

During its first forty-seven years, the League raised some $13,000,000 for the purchase of redwood lands, and the State of California supplied an additional $13,000,000. This money permitted the purchase of 100,000 acres of land, two-thirds of which represents virgin stands of great redwoods. It would cost at least $250,000,000 to purchase this acreage at today's prices.

All of this land has been turned over to the State of California by the League, with the understanding that the state will protect the trees, "preserve their naturalness, enhance their beauty, and increase their usefulness and inspiration to nature-lovers all over the world." There are twenty-eight state redwood parks in California, ranging in size from the 11.8 acres of the Paul M. Dimmick Memorial Grove near Mendocino to the 37,000 acres of Humboldt Redwoods State Park. The parks are strung in a patchwork of isolated areas along hundreds of miles of the California coast, but the best ones are located along California's "Redwood Highway," U.S. 101.

Four of these parks, spaced over 150 miles, contain the majority of the trees saved so far. The largest and southernmost, Humboldt Redwoods State Park, 240 miles north of San Francisco, was established in 1921 out of the first purchases of the League. Here, in Founders Grove, is the famed Founders Tree, long considered the tallest of redwoods, though now barely in the top ten; and nearby is Bull Creek Flat, one of the finest of all redwood stands, whose 9,400 acres were bought with the aid of a $2,000,000 gift from John D. Rockefeller, Jr., in 1931. U.S. 101 winds through the eastern side of Humboldt Park; there are two roads, one old and one new, and those who love the redwoods take the old one, known as "the Avenue of the Giants." It is a slow two-lane road, lightly traveled, that passes almost like a tunnel through dark redwood groves. The branches of the trees meet far overhead; and if one must pass among redwoods by car at all, this is the way to do it. Running parallel to the Avenue of the Giants is the new U.S. 101, dedicated

Humboldt Redwood State Park

in 1960. It is a modern four-lane freeway that slashes brutally through the park's borders. Riding along it at 65 or 70 miles an hour, one sees a great many redwoods very quickly, but one does not really see them at all.

On the Avenue of the Giants, just north of Humboldt Park, are six miles of redwoods as beautiful as any in the park. Until recently, most visitors to the park assumed that these trees *were* in the park; but in fact they were privately held, the property of the Pacific Lumber Company. Since 1926 the Save-the-Redwoods League has worked to preserve this narrow 1,400-acre tract as an extension of the Avenue of the Giants, and in August 1967 the League announced that negotiations had been completed for its purchase. The price—reflecting the sharp rise in redwood values—was a staggering $7,000,000. Half of this money was to come from the Federal Land and Water Conservation Fund; the State of California was contributing $1,925,000, and the remaining $1,575,000 would come from the League, which is to say from the donations of private citizens.

Continuing north on U.S. 101, the traveler comes next to Prairie Creek Redwoods State Park, about 35 miles north of Eureka, California. Prairie Creek is valued by naturalists because it preserves the whole range of redwood country from the low inland mountains to the edge of the Pacific. Aside from its handsome redwoods, the park contains such splendors as the 250-foot-high Gold Bluffs, a magnificent stretch of unspoiled seashore, and lovely Fern Canyon, whose walls are brocaded with thick growths of the rare five-finger fern. Fern Canyon was added to the park in 1956 as a result of a Save-the-Redwoods League fund-raising effort. Another exceptional feature of this park is its herd of Roosevelt elk, nearly extinct elsewhere. Redwood Creek Valley, where the tallest known redwoods grow, lies a few miles southeast of Prairie Creek Park. Though the property belongs to the Arcata Redwood Company, a timber firm, the trees are not being cut. And the forest, though difficult to reach, is open to the public.

A short distance north of Prairie Creek, but separated from it by about twenty miles of privately held land, is Del Norte Coast Redwoods State Park, established in 1925. This 6,000-acre park is one of the few remaining places where it is possible to see redwoods of great size growing right along the Pacific shore. It lies 8 miles south of Crescent City, California.

When U.S. 101 reaches Crescent City, it turns inland at a sharp angle and leads to the northernmost of the parks, Jedediah Smith Redwoods State Park, founded in 1929. This 10,000-acre park, named for the first white man to explore this part of California, early in the nineteenth century, contains one of the densest redwood groves of all. The best way to see Jed Smith Park by car is to take the Howland Hill Road, a back-country one-lane route that branches off from U.S. 199, a road that runs northeast of the park and winds westward toward Crescent City. Passing completely across the park, Howland Hill Road is flanked all the way by vast redwood trees, so close to the road that they seem to graze a car's fenders. There are no signs along the way, no buildings, no telephone lines, no trace of man's hand at all, except the road itself. Occasional turn-out spaces are provided for those infrequent occasions when one meets a car coming from the other direction.

These are the main redwood parks. There are two dozen others, such as Brannon Island Park, 70 miles inland and the easternmost of the redwood parks, and Richardson Grove Park, an unusually fine one south of Humboldt Park, and the Standish-Hickey Park, in Leggett Valley. Nearly all these parks are bordered by privately owned redwood stands, and attempts are being made by the Save-the-Redwoods League and other conservationist groups to purchase these stands and add them to the park. Some of the League's efforts have been successful, as in the purchase of the Pacific Lumber Company's property along the Avenue of the Giants. Other important groves are being held intact by lumber companies, despite the high taxes they must pay on the uncut timber, while conservationists try to raise money to buy them. But prices are mounting. In the 1960's the Save-the-Redwoods League added 44 acres to Prairie Creek Park—paying as much for those 44 acres as it had for 1,500 for the park's original 6,000 acres, forty years before!

Not all the timber companies are willing to be patient. Along one boundary of Prairie Creek Park it is easy to see where the park ends and private holdings begin, for the trees bordering the park have been cut away as though with a giant's razor, right up to the edge of the park line. The park's outside row of trees stands as a palisade along the border, and just beyond is a wasteland extending thousands of acres.

Why save more redwoods at all? Close to 70,000 acres of fine trees are preserved already in California's parks, nearly five times the *total* acreage occupied by the giant sequoias of the Sierra Nevada. Isn't that enough?

Some Californians feel that it is. They include Governor Ronald Reagan, who during his 1966 election campaign, when asked how he felt about expanding the redwood parks, replied, "A tree's a tree—how many more do you need to look at?" The lumber companies, even those who have supported the conservationist measures up till now, oppose further expansion of the parks, other than adding small and

Jedediah Smith Park

134

exceptional groves here and there. They argue that their investment in sawmills and processing plants will be wiped out if they are forced to give up as much redwood forest as some conservationists ask. The employees of the lumber companies, who stand to lose their jobs if the privately held forests become parks, also are hostile to the idea of bigger parks. "Do you believe in freedom?" a guard at the Miller Redwood Company near Crescent City asked a newspaper interviewer in 1967. "If you do, you're not for the park plan. It's not freedom when they can come in and take a man's business away from him. . . . God made trees for people to use. There's plenty more around here for people to look at if they want to."

How many redwoods are enough redwoods?

Of the original 2,000,000 acres of virgin redwoods, 85 percent have already been cut. New trees are growing on some of that acreage, and some of them are already 90 or 100 feet high, but they are a long way from replacing the vanished giants. Of the remaining 15 percent, a little more than 3 percent are held in the California state parks. The rest are scheduled for cutting, and the U.S. Forest Service estimates that they will all be gone by 1980, except for those few groves currently marked for eventual transfer to park status.

Is 4 percent of the original redwood forest enough to save? Perhaps it might be, if there were a single continuous redwood park of 80,000 acres somewhere. But because the redwoods are scattered over so many small parks, even these "saved" trees are vulnerable to dangers that mere arithmetic does not show.

No matter how large a redwood park is, the trees within it are not safe so long as logging is permitted to proceed on a business-as-usual basis along its borders. This was grimly demonstrated in 1955 in the biggest redwood park of all, Humboldt.

The incomparable Rockefeller Forest of Humboldt Park was purchased in 1931. It consists of a 9,400-acre section of the Bull Creek Basin, a 26,000-acre region of deep canyons, steep slopes, and fast-rushing streams. In its natural state, Bull Creek Basin experienced occasional floods after heavy winter rains, but suffered no significant amount of soil erosion. The roots of the redwoods and other trees and shrubs anchored the soil and soaked up excess water. The floods did no harm to the trees, and actually aided them by depositing fertile silt around them.

It was impossible to purchase the entire Bull Creek Basin. The choice Rockefeller Forest section alone was added to Humboldt Park, and the remaining two-thirds of the basin stayed in private hands. Logging operations began on the privately owned land in 1947. In a careless and wanton way the loggers stripped the hillsides of virtually all trees, ripping out everything that could be cut into marketable boards. What the loggers left, fire destroyed. By 1955 much of the Bull Creek Basin beyond the Rockefeller Forest had been transformed into an empty, barren ruin.

The rains came in December 1955. No trees remained to slow the runoff. No roots drank up the torrents. Down from the highest slopes of the watershed rushed a fierce, angry wall of water, scraping away the topsoil and the gravel and rock beneath it. Landslides began; tons of gravel tumbled into swollen streams and were swept away toward the low-lying Rockefeller Forest. Into the flatlands of the Bull Creek Basin came this unchecked and uncheckable flood, and within a few hours 500 huge trees had tumbled into Bull Creek, forming a log jam 40 feet high that dammed the creek and sent more water spilling over its banks. Ninety-nine more trees were so badly undercut by the flood that they had to be removed before the creek itself could be cleared. Other trees were choked by the gravel and other debris that the flood dumped on their roots. The disaster undid the growth of centuries in a single day. And it would not have happened had the upper reaches of Bull Creek Basin been left unharmed.

After the 1955 calamity, a state reforestation program was belatedly begun to cover the bald slopes with new trees. Dams were built in upper Bull Creek Basin. The Save-the-Redwoods League raised more than a million dollars to buy land above the Rockefeller Forest—not because that land contained a single attractive tree, but merely to protect the trees along lower Bull Creek. By the end of 1964, almost 15,000 acres had been acquired and given to the state. Even that was not enough for full protection. Nearly 3,000 acres of cut-over land remained still in the eroded condition in which the loggers had left it; and when heavy rains came again in January 1965, a new flood knocked over almost 300 more redwoods. Fewer than half of these, though, were really large trees, and there is reason to hope that this will be the last such disaster at Bull Creek.

The lesson of Bull Creek is that buying redwood groves is not enough. Entire watersheds must be brought under public control. Thus, when word came in 1966 that a lumber company was erecting a large new sawmill on Mill Creek, upstream from Jedediah Smith Park, conservationists warned that logging in the Mill Creek watershed might imperil the Jed Smith redwoods, and called for an extension of the park to take in the upstream area.

Conservationists also wonder how safe the trees are in the possession of the State of California. Many of California's governors, rightly recognizing the unique value of the redwood parks, have defended them against those who want to limit or destroy them; but such statements as Governor Reagan's "A tree's a tree" have led to misgivings—so far unfounded—over the future of the state parks.

Even the friends of the trees are capable of harming them. Governor Reagan's predecessor, Edmund G. Brown, was a supporter of conservationist ideas, and wished to make the trees more easily accessible to appreciative visitors. Governor Brown's way of giving the trees to the public was to authorize the widening of U.S. 101 into a high-speed freeway running right through the parks.

The first leg of this four-lane freeway was dedicated in Humboldt Park in August 1960. Governor Brown told the notables who attended the ceremony that the new road "will lead through one of the most beautiful parts of California and the world. . . . A basic premise is to open up new vistas to Californians and our millions of visitors from other states and nations. . . .

"What we have done here will be done elsewhere in the redwoods—at Prairie Creek, Jedediah Smith and Richardson Grove. . . ."

Conservationists were appalled. The Humboldt Creek section of the freeway had created a 60-foot-wide gouge through the forest; hundreds of giant redwoods had been cut down to make way for it, and vast expanses of hard pavement appeared on the banks of rivers. The Save-the-Redwoods League was bombarded with angry letters from contributors who had *not* given money to buy land for superhighways. Governor Brown began to realize that the Humboldt Park freeway had been a mistake, and vowed that future widenings of U.S. 101 would have to go around, not through, the northern parks.

But the California Division of Highways acted for a

while as though it had the last word on where the freeway would go. In 1963, its engineers recommended building two 3,000-foot freeway sections through the largest grove of Jedediah Smith Park. This grove, known as the National Tribute Grove, was purchased by the state for $469,000, with a third of the money coming from the Save-the-Redwoods League treasury, a third from the State of California, and the rest from about 4,000 persons throughout the country who wished to establish a redwood memorial for friends or relatives killed in World War II. To the south, the freeway was to run along the top of Gold Bluffs in Prairie Creek Park, or else along the beach at the base of the bluffs—in either case, the result would be a mutilation of the park.

The Save-the-Redwoods League threatened to go to court, if necessary, to protect the parks, and for the time being the highway expansion plans were halted. But how long could automobile-conscious California hold out against the demand for a new freeway? Across the nation a cry arose to take the redwood parks away from the state and turn them into a Redwood National Park.

Such a park had been urged for more than seventy years. The California-based Sierra Club, a conservationist organization founded in 1892 by John Muir, had called from its earliest years for the redwoods to be taken over by the Federal Government. The Save-the-Redwoods League's first public statement had included a call for a Redwood National Park. In 1920 Congress had authorized a survey of the redwood region to determine the best site for a national park. The survey report recommended a 64,000-acre park on the lower Klamath River, near the Oregon border, but nothing was done. Congresswoman Helen Gahagan Douglas of California introduced a bill in 1946 that would have established a "Franklin Delano Roosevelt Memorial Redwood

Forest" of 2,500,000 acres, taking in 180,000 acres of the redwood belt, but the bill got nowhere.

The Federal Government, which owns almost all of the giant sequoias, has only two small redwood holdings, and only one of these is under real protection. That is little Muir Woods National Monument near San Francisco. The other government redwood property is the 15,000-acre Northern California Redwood Forest, east and north of the city of Klamath, which has had an odd and troubled history.

In 1936, Congress authorized the U.S. Forest Service to purchase forest land in northern California. This was meant as a form of Depression relief, an injection of government cash into a poverty-stricken region. The law set up two "purchase units"—one of 600,000 acres south of the city of Mendocino, and one of 263,000 acres near the Oregon border. No purchases were ever made in the southern unit. In the northern unit, the Forest Service began buying land in 1939, and in twenty-eight separate transactions over the following six years accumulated the 15,000 acres, lying between Del Norte Coast Redwoods State Park and Prairie Creek Redwoods State Park, for a total of only $44,000.

But land controlled by the Forest Service is not deemed sacred, as is land run by the National Park Service. The Forest Service works with lumber companies to develop more efficient and productive methods of logging, and that is what has been going on in the Northern California Redwood Forest since 1945. About 1,000 acres of the tract are set aside for experiments in seeding and logging; the rest of the land is open to "harvesting" by lumber companies. In 1966, for example, the Forest Service permitted private companies to cut 17.6 million board feet of lumber in this forest—partly redwood, partly Douglas fir.

The Sierra Club and other similar groups have denounced

this, on the grounds that *no* redwoods in government hands should be cut; the United States, they say, can well afford to do without the few millions of dollars that have been earned by selling lumber from this forest. However, it is generally agreed that the Northern California Redwood Forest is not really suitable to become a major redwood park, since it contains a mixed stand of timber rather than the virgin redwood groves whose protection is most important.

The struggle to establish a Redwood National Park turned in other directions. By 1964, the idea was under serious consideration in Washington for the first time in decades. However, it promptly became entangled in disputes. Not only did the lumber companies protest the park idea—which was only to be expected—but rival conservationist groups indulged in bickering over the site of a park, and succeeded in confusing the issue thoroughly.

The National Park Service, which conducted a detailed survey of the redwood region in 1963, issued a report the following year calling for the establishment of a park in the Redwood Creek-Prairie Creek area. This park would include the privately owned Redwood Creek Valley redwoods, where the tallest of all trees had been discovered, and would incorporate the existing Prairie Creek Redwoods State Park. The National Park Service report declared that the Redwood Creek area contains "the largest uncut block of virgin growth not preserved—certainly the most significant large block in terms of park values. . . . Lower Redwood Creek from ridge to ridge is essentially uncut. It presents an outstanding redwood valley picture. . . ."

This plan won the support of the influential Sierra Club, and in the 90th Congress sixty-one members of the Senate

Del Norte redwoods, in the newly formed Redwood National Park.

and House of Representatives sponsored bills that would create a 90,000-acre national park in this location. Objections came at once from the Arcata Redwood Company, which said it would be forced out of business by the park, and from four other companies that would be seriously hurt. "We will fight to retain our timberlands," said Arcata's president, Howard A. Libbey, "and for the right to carry on our operations for many years in the best interests of the company, its employees, and the communities in which we do business. . . . There are many enterprises, including school districts, which depend heavily upon the continuation of the operations of this company from a standpoint of taxes, etc."

While the Redwood Creek debate was getting under way, the Save-the-Redwoods League was arguing for a national park about 150 miles to the north. Mindful of the 1955 Bull Creek disaster, the League wanted to safeguard Jedediah Smith's redwoods by having the Government buy the privately owned Mill Creek watershed outside the park.

Secretary of the Interior Stewart Udall, the most powerful conservationist figure in the Government, gave his support to the Mill Creek plan. At Secretary Udall's urging, President Johnson asked Congress on February 23, 1966, to establish a Redwood National Park of 43,000 acres, consisting of Jedediah Smith and Del Norte Coast parks plus the Mill Creek land, which would be bought from the Miller Redwood Company.

The Miller company objected. So did a number of California citizens who did not like the idea of turning state parks over to the Government. The Sierra Club protested that it was more important to save the tall trees of Redwood Creek. Some Congressmen criticized an unusual feature of the proposal which would give Del Norte County, California, about $340,000 a year for five years in place of the tax money it would lose when the Miller Redwood Company went out of business. Never before had such an arrangement been included in the terms for purchasing land for a national park.

The battle between the Sierra Club and the Save-the-Redwoods League played into the hands of certain Congressmen who did not wish to see any park whatever established. So long as the conservationists disagreed, they said, why should we get mixed up in the fight? Other Congressmen, who *did* want a Redwood National Park, were perturbed by the costs involved. The Mill Creek plan would cost $55,000,000—the most ever spent on a national park. Not only would the Government have to buy land; it would also have to buy out a hundred private homeowners just north of Jedediah Smith Park, and reimburse the Miller Redwood Company millions of dollars for a newly built sawmill. On the other hand, the Redwood Creek plan was even more expensive: an estimated $140,000,000. With the nation staggering under the costs of the war in Vietnam, could it afford more millions to buy trees?

During the debate, the Sierra Club took full-page advertisements in many newspapers to show that the "expense" of the Redwood Creek park would be about 75 cents per American. "History will think it most strange," the ads declared, "that America could afford the Moon and $4-billion airplanes while a patch of primeval redwoods—not too big for a man to walk through in a day—was considered beyond its means." However, recognizing the political realities of the situation, the Sierra Club told Congress in the summer of 1966 that it would settle for a park smaller than the 90,000-acre one proposed by the National Park Service. Time was running out for the trees; if $55,000,000 was the most that could be spent for the park, let it be spent for the biggest possible park at Redwood Creek.

The jockeying between the Mill Creek and Redwood

Creek factions continued all through 1966. While Congress hesitated, lumber companies at both sites tried to force the issue. The Arcata Redwood Company and the Georgia-Pacific Corporation, which owned land around Redwood Creek, speeded up logging operations. The Miller Redwood Company began to cut virgin redwoods along the southern boundary of the Jedediah Smith Park, inside the proposed Mill Creek national park—"cutting out its heart," according to Senator Thomas Kuchel of California.

The Miller company's cutting in particular so angered President Johnson that he asked Congress to forbid by law any logging in the Mill Creek area. Hastily Miller agreed to halt its logging operations there until the question of the national park was decided; Arcata and Georgia-Pacific promised to leave the great redwoods of Redwood Creek untouched also until matters were resolved.

In the hope of putting a halt to quarreling among conservationists, the Save-the-Redwoods League issued this moderate statement: "We support a Redwood National Park of maximum size . . . containing the best virgin forests in private ownership whether in Redwood Creek, Mill Creek or elsewhere. . . . We will support the National Park Service in its recommendations." The League added that the Mill Creek watershed "in our judgment is preeminently worthy of National Park status and we have supported it. Nevertheless we will also support any other projects that will preserve Redwoods."

Out of the debate, later in 1967, came a compromise plan sponsored by Senators Kuchel of California and Jackson of Washington. Their bill would have created a 61,000-acre national park spanning 40 miles of the California coast from Orick to Crescent City, straddling U.S. 101. It would have taken in portions of Prairie Creek, Del Norte Coast, and Jedediah Smith state parks, amounting to 27,000 acres in all, with land purchased from private owners to link the three state parks, now separated from one another. North of Jed Smith, the park would have taken in the Mill Creek watershed by the purchase of 5,700 acres of Miller Redwood Company land and 845 acres from the Simpson Timber Company. A separate southern unit of the park would protect the tall trees of Redwood Creek through the purchase of the Arcata and Georgia-Pacific holdings.

The Kuchel-Jackson plan made the most of the difficult situation. It did not create the large, continuous national park that some conservationists hoped for, but it would have rescued the vital Mill Creek and Redwood Creek districts, leaving hope that in later years the rest of the surrounding land might be incorporated into the park. The Senate passed this bill in November 1967. However, the House of Representatives chose to take no action on it for nearly a year thereafter, preventing the park from coming into being.

During that year of delay the logging continued. Despite the promises made in 1966, one lumber company resumed cutting in December 1967 along a Redwood Creek area called the Emerald Mile, where rows of 300-foot trees rise in a wondrous wall on both sides of the creek. "Yes, America's majestic redwoods have already been saved," this company said in newspaper advertisements justifying its action. It asserted that there was no real need to add more park area to the existing acreage; besides, it said, "It is necessary for us to do some harvesting in this area in order to run our plants on an economically sound basis." The Sierra Club promptly retaliated with angry advertisements headed LEGISLATION BY CHAIN-SAW?

In the summer of 1968 the House of Representatives finally produced its own bill for a Redwood National Park. It called not for the 61,000 acres approved by the Senate, but for a mere 28,500 acres, taken mostly from the existing state parks. A Sierra Club spokesman called the proposal "shocking," saying, "There's no core of a park. It's all appendages without any main body." But last-minute negotiations produced a happier ending. In September 1968, House and Senate conferees agreed on a single park bill much closer to the original Senate plan than to the shrunken House version.

The Redwood National Park bill, passed by Congress on September 19, 1968, and sent to President Johnson for signature, authorized a 58,000-acre park costing $92,000,000 —more than all other national parks combined had cost. It includes, subject to donation by the State of California, 27,500 acres of Jed Smith, Del Norte, and Prairie Creek state parks, and more than 30,000 acres of timberland now in private hands. A 33-mile-long corridor along the Pacific will connect the major units of the park. The moment the President signed the bill, the privately held redwoods passed into government ownership, and all logging ceased forever at Redwood Creek Valley and the other endangered sites.

The giant sequoias of the Sierra Nevada—the ones that remain—have been spared for the astonishment of those who follow us. Now, thousands of acres of virgin redwoods —out of the original millions—have also been spared, and will not be turned into lawn furniture and bungalow porches. It is little enough to have saved, out of all that plenty, but it was a bitter struggle to save even that. These amazing trees belong, not to the lumber companies of California, not even to the citizens of California or the United States, but to all the world. They were here before man himself existed. Nothing remotely like them exists anywhere else on earth. We have destroyed many of the finest of these trees; now we hold the remaining ones in trust for future generations. May it not be said of us in times to come that it was a trust betrayed.

Appendix:

Where to See Giant Sequoias and Redwoods

GIANT SEQUOIAS

Living examples of *Sequoia gigantea* grow in many parts of the British Isles, in France, in Spain, in Switzerland, in Germany, and even in Zagreb, Yugoslavia. But these all were planted in the nineteenth century and, while of fairly large size, are far being being true giants. In the United States, attempts to grow the giant sequoia outside California have generally been failures. One tree, planted on the shore of Lake Cayuga, New York, lived 70 years and grew to a height of 70 feet, but was killed by the severe winter of 1933–34. Several trees planted at the Arnold Arboretum, Boston, died before they had passed the 6-foot mark. An exception is a tree at the Tyler Arboretum near Lima, Pennsylvania, which was thriving at last report and had exceeded 50 feet in height.

The only place to see authentic giant sequoias is in California, where they are on view in three national parks, one state park, and several national forests. These are the most easily reached groves:

Kings Canyon National Park

General Grant Grove. Site of many of the largest trees. Big Stump Grove. Completely cut over, but young trees are growing. The Adam Stump, remnant of one of the biggest trees ever cut, is located here.

Redwood Canyon Forest. Large thickly populated stand of giant sequoias of all sizes and ages.

Sequoia National Park

Giant Forest. Finest of all existing giant sequoia groves, contains the world's largest tree (the General Sherman) and many others of great size.

Muir Grove. A beautiful 450-acre grove in the northwest section of the park.

A dozen other groves, some accessible only by trail, are located in this park.

Yosemite National Park

Mariposa Grove. Contains the Grizzly Giant, and more than 200 other trees 10 feet or more in diameter. One of the most frequently visited groves.

Merced Grove. Contains 20 large trees.

Tuolumne Grove. Contains 25 large trees, plus the Dead Giant, 29½ feet in diameter.

Calaveras Big Trees State Park

Calaveras Grove (State Highway 4, Calaveras County), consisting of more than 50 acres of giant sequoias, was discovered by A. T. Dowd in 1852.

Stanislaus or South Calaveras Grove, five miles to the south, contains 947 giant sequoias, many of large size.

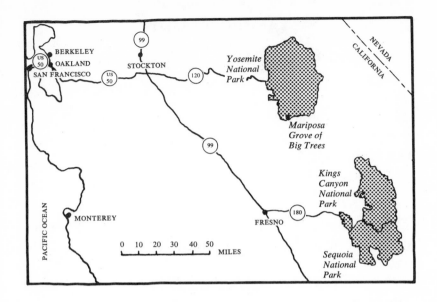

Sierra National Forest

Nelder Grove, partly cut in the nineteenth century and later burned, is still worth seeing. It is located about 5 miles south of Yosemite's Mariposa Grove.

Sequoia National Forest

Boole Tree Grove. Almost completely cut over and then burned, still contains one of the largest trees in the world.

Mountain Home Forest. Contains several hundred big trees, many of unusual interest.

There are about ten other groves in Sequoia National Forest. Some are accessible only by trail; others are virtually inaccessible.

REDWOODS

It is possible to see redwood trees growing along most of the California coast, and there are some in Europe. The stands of giant redwoods are found in 28 state parks and

151

one national monument, all in California. The most important of these are:

Jedediah Smith Redwoods State Park

Northernmost of the state parks, near Crescent City, on U.S. 199.

Del Norte Coast Redwoods State Park

Eight miles south of Crescent City, on U.S. 101. Outstanding ocean views.

Prairie Creek Redwoods State Park

Six miles north of Orick, on U.S. 101. Home of a notable herd of Roosevelt elk.
Fern Canyon is a special feature worth visiting.

Humboldt Redwoods State Park

Largest of the redwood preserves; 240 miles north of San Francisco. It contains Rockefeller Forest, Founders Grove, and the Avenue of the Giants Parkway.

Richardson Grove State Park

Nine miles south of Garberville on U.S. 101. Excellent redwood stands of about 750 acres.

Petrified Forest State Park

Fifteen miles east of Santa Rosa. Has fossilized redwood trunks millions of years old strewn among living trees.

Muir Woods National Monument

Most accessible of all the redwood groves, a short distance from San Francisco, in Marin County.

Big Basin Redwoods State Park

Near the southern limits of the redwood range, 23 miles northwest of Santa Cruz, contains more than 11,000 acres of trees.

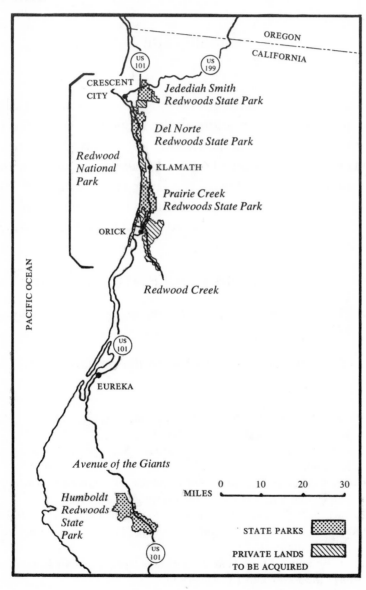

153

Bibliography

The two conservationist groups most closely connected with the study and preservation of the sequoias are the Sierra Club and the Save-the-Redwoods League. Both organizations are more concerned with the redwoods than with the giant sequoias, since few of the latter are in danger of logging. The organizations publish many books and pamphlets on the sequoias, and are in need of funds to continue their work. For more details, write:

SAVE-THE-REDWOODS LEAGUE, 114 Sansome Street, San Francisco, California 94104.
SIERRA CLUB, 1050 Mills Tower, San Francisco, California 94104.

Books and periodicals consulted in the preparation of this book include:

Brown, Andrew H., "Saving Earth's Oldest Living Things." *National Geographic Magazine*, May, 1951.
Chaney, Ralph W., *Redwoods of the Past*. San Francisco, Save-the-Redwoods League, 1965.
Cook, Lawrence F., *The Giant Sequoias of California*. Washington, United States Government Printing Office, 1955.
Ellsworth, R. S., *The Giant Sequoia*. Oakland, J. D. Berger, 1924.
Farquhar, Francis P., "California's Big Trees." *The American West*, Summer, 1965.
Fritz, Emanuel, *Story Told by a Fallen Redwood*. San Francisco, Save-the-Redwoods League, 1934.

Bibliography

Fry, Walter, and White, J. R., *Big Trees*. Stanford, Stanford University Press, 1930.

Gannett, Henry, "The Redwood Forest of the Pacific Coast." *National Geographic Magazine*, May, 1899.

Grant, Madison, "Saving the Redwoods." *National Geographic Magazine*, June, 1920.

Hartesveldt, Richard J., "Fire Ecology of the Giant Sequoias." *Natural History*, December, 1964.

Hyde, Philip, and Leydet, François, *The Last Redwoods*. San Francisco, Sierra Club, 1963.

Hylander, Clarence J., *The World of Plant Life*. New York, The Macmillan Company, 1944.

Jane, F. W., "The Dawn Redwood." *New Biology* 16, April, 1954.

Jepson, W. L., *The Trees of California*. Berkeley, University of California, 1923.

———, *Trees, Shrubs and Flowers of the Redwood Region*. San Francisco, Save-the-Redwoods League, 1934.

Kauffmann, John Michael, "Giant Sequoias Draw Millions to California Parks." *National Geographic Magazine*, August, 1959.

Kilburn, Paul D., "Endangered Relic Trees." *Natural History*, December, 1961.

Menninger, Edwin A., *Fantastic Trees*. New York, The Viking Press, Inc., 1967.

Merriam, John C., *A Living Link in History*. San Francisco, Save-the-Redwoods League, 1934.

Muir, John, *The Mountains of California*. New York, Century Co., 1894.

Nelson, Bryce, "The Coast Redwoods: Struggle over National Park Proposals." *Science*, September 30, 1966.

Sherwood, George H., *The Big Tree and Its Story*. New York, American Museum of Natural History, 1929.

Silverberg, Robert, *Ghost Towns of the American West*. New York, Thomas Y. Crowell Co., 1968.

Taylor, Norman, *The Ageless Relicts: The Story of Sequoia*. New York, St. Martin's Press, Inc., 1963.

Zahl, Paul A., "Finding the Mt. Everest of All Living Things." *National Geographic Magazine*, July, 1964.

Index

Italic page numbers indicate illustrations.

INDEX

INDEX

INDEX